MATHEMATICS

f E

STUD OK

T

Causeway Press Limited

Published by Causeway Press Ltd
P.O. Box 13, Ormskirk, Lancashire L39 5HP

First published 2003

British Library Cataloguing-in-Publication Data.
A catalogue record for this book is available from the British Library.

ISBN 1-902796-39-X

Acknowledgements
Past exam questions, provided by *London Examinations, A Division of Edexcel*, are marked Edexcel.
The answers to all questions are entirely the responsibility of the authors/publisher and have neither been
provided nor approved by Edexcel.

Every effort has been made to locate the copyright owners of material used in this book.
Any omissions brought to the notice of the publisher are regretted and will be credited in
subsequent printings.

Page design
Billy Johnson

Reader
Anne Alcock

Artwork
David Alcorn

Cover design
Waring-Collins Partnership

Typesetting by Billy Johnson, San Francisco, California, USA

Printed and bound by Scotprint, Haddington, Scotland

preface

This book provides detailed revision notes, worked examples and examination questions to support students in their preparation for Edexcel GCSE Mathematics at the Higher Tier of Entry.

The book has been designed so that it can be used in conjunction with the companion book *Mathematics for Edexcel GCSE - Higher Tier* or as a stand-alone revision book for self study and provides full coverage of Edexcel Specification A and Edexcel Specification B (Modular).

In preparing the text, full account has been made of the requirements for students to be able to use and apply mathematics in written examination papers and be able to solve problems in mathematics both with and without a calculator.

The detailed revision notes, worked examples and examination questions have been organised into 40 self-contained sections which meet the requirements of the National Curriculum and provide efficient coverage of the specifications.

Sections 1 - 9   Number
Sections 10 - 22   Algebra
Sections 23 - 34   Shape, Space and Measures
Sections 35 - 40   Handling Data

At the end of the sections on Number, Algebra, Shape, Space and Measures and Handling Data, section reviews are provided to give further opportunities to consolidate skills.

At the end of the book there is a final examination questions section with a further compilation of exam and exam-style questions, organised for non-calculator and calculator practice, in preparation for the exams.

contents

Number

Algebra

Shape, Space and Measures

Sections 23 - 34

Handling Data

Sections 35 - 40

Whole Numbers ●●●●●●●●●

What you need to know

- You should be able to read and write numbers expressed in figures and words.

- Be able to recognise the place value of each digit in a number.
  Eg 1 In the number 5384 the digit 8 is worth 80, but in the number 4853 the digit 8 is worth 800.

- Know the Multiplication Tables up to 10×10.

- Use non-calculator methods for addition, subtraction, multiplication and division.

- Know the order of operations in a calculation.

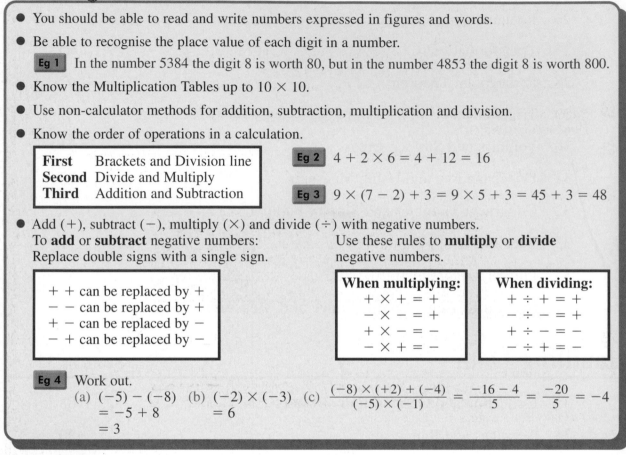

First	Brackets and Division line
Second	Divide and Multiply
Third	Addition and Subtraction

Eg 2 $4 + 2 \times 6 = 4 + 12 = 16$

Eg 3 $9 \times (7 - 2) + 3 = 9 \times 5 + 3 = 45 + 3 = 48$

- Add (+), subtract (−), multiply (×) and divide (÷) with negative numbers.
  To **add** or **subtract** negative numbers: Use these rules to **multiply** or **divide**
  Replace double signs with a single sign.   negative numbers.

+ + can be replaced by +
− − can be replaced by +
+ − can be replaced by −
− + can be replaced by −

When multiplying:
+ × + = +
− × − = +
+ × − = −
− × + = −

When dividing:
+ ÷ + = +
− ÷ − = +
+ ÷ − = −
− ÷ + = −

Eg 4 Work out.
(a) $(-5) - (-8)$ (b) $(-2) \times (-3)$ (c) $\dfrac{(-8) \times (+2) + (-4)}{(-5) \times (-1)} = \dfrac{-16 - 4}{5} = \dfrac{-20}{5} = -4$
$\quad = -5 + 8 \qquad\qquad = 6$
$\quad = 3$

Exercise 1   Do not use a calculator for this exercise.

1 (a) Write one million five thousand and ten in figures.
   (b) Given that $235 \times 640 = 150\,400$, work out $1\,504\,000 \div 64$.

2 Work out.   (a) $7096 + 2974$ (b) $8042 - 1357$ (c) 731×137 (d) $2002 \div 13$

3 (a) Using each of the digits 9, 2, 3 and 6 write down
      (i) the largest odd number,   (ii) the smallest even number.
   (b) What is the answer when the smallest even number is subtracted from the largest odd number?

4 Last year Mr Alderton had the following household bills.

Gas	£364	Electricity	£158	Telephone	£187
Water	£244	Insurance	£236	Council Tax	£983

He paid the bills by 12 equal monthly payments. How much was each monthly payment?

5 Colin packs shirts in a factory. He packs 85 shirts a day.
   Last year he packed shirts for 218 days. How many shirts did he pack last year?

6 Work out 453×73.

Edexcel

7 Naomi has collected £357 from her friends for concert tickets. The tickets cost £17 each. How many people have paid for tickets?

8 Work out.
(a) $12 - 6 + 2$
(b) $12 \div 6 \times 2$
(c) $(27 + 8) \times 3$
(d) $\dfrac{9 - 4 + 3 \times 5}{2 \times 3 + 4}$

9 Tom breeds hamsters for pet shops.
The number of hamsters trebles each year.
Tom has 20 hamsters at the end of Year 1.
(a) How many hamsters would Tom have at the end of 5 years?
(b) A hamster cage can hold no more than 14 hamsters.
Work out the minimum number of cages needed for 900 hamsters.

Edexcel

10 Simon is 8 kg heavier than Matt. Their weights add up to 132 kg.
How heavy is Simon?

11 A roll of wire is 500 cm long. From the roll, Debra cuts 3 pieces which each measure 75 cm and 4 pieces which each measure 40 cm. How much wire is left on the roll?

12 Car Hire Co. have the following cars available to rent.

Model	Number of cars	Weekly rental
Corsa	10	£210
Astra	12	£255
Zafira	6	£289

Work out the total weekly rental when all the cars are hired.

13 Calculate.
(a) $\dfrac{10 \times 20 \times 30 \times 40 \times 50}{1 + 2 + 3 + 4 + 5}$
(b) $\dfrac{356 - 200 \div 25}{24}$

14 This rule can be used to estimate the temperature in °F for temperatures given in °C.

> Multiply the temperature in °C by 2 and add 30.

Use this rule to estimate -17°C in °F.

15 Work out.
(a) $(-9) - (-5) + (-3)$
(b) $\dfrac{(-7) \times (-3) - (-6)}{(-9)}$
(c) $\dfrac{(-3) \times (-5) - (-7) \times (+3)}{(-4) + (-2)}$

16 A test has 12 questions.

> A correct answer scores $+3$ marks.   An incorrect answer scores -1 mark.

Pippa attempts every question and scores 8 marks.
How many correct answers did she get?

17 The number of bacteria in a certain colony doubles every day.
At the start of an experiment there are 96 bacteria.
How many bacteria will there be 10 days later?

18 The prizes paid out in last Saturday's Lottery are shown in the table.

Number of winners	Value of each prize
1	£6 469 676
27	£73 728
708	£1 757
41 422	£66
812 558	£10

How much was paid out in prizes in last Saturday's Lottery?

Decimals and Fractions ● ● ●

What you need to know

● You should be able to use non-calculator methods for addition, subtraction, multiplication and division of decimals.

Eg 1 Work out.

(a) 5.1×0.43

$$\begin{array}{r} 5.1 \quad \text{(1 d.p.)} \\ \times \quad 0.43 \quad \text{(2 d.p.)} \\ \hline 153 \leftarrow 51 \times 3 \\ + 2040 \leftarrow 51 \times 40 \\ \hline 2.193 \quad \text{(3 d.p.)} \end{array}$$

(b) $1.64 \div 0.2$

$$\frac{1.64}{0.2} = \frac{16.4}{2} = 8.2$$

When a number is **multiplied** by a number between 0 and 1 the result will be **smaller** than the original number.
When a number is **divided** by a number between 0 and 1 the result will be **larger** than the original number.

● The top number of a fraction is called the **numerator**, the bottom number is called the **denominator**.

● $2\frac{1}{2}$ is an example of a **mixed number**. It is a mixture of whole numbers and fractions.

● $\frac{5}{2}$ is an **improper** (or 'top heavy') fraction.

● Fractions must have the **same denominator** before **adding** or **subtracting**.

Eg 2 Work out.

(a) $\frac{3}{4} + \frac{2}{3} = \frac{9}{12} + \frac{8}{12} = \frac{17}{12} = 1\frac{5}{12}$

(b) $\frac{4}{5} - \frac{1}{2} = \frac{8}{10} - \frac{5}{10} = \frac{3}{10}$

Add (or subtract) the numerators only. When the answer is an improper fraction change it into a mixed number.

● Mixed numbers must be changed to **improper fractions** before **multiplying** or **dividing**.

Eg 3 Work out.

(a) $1\frac{1}{4} \times 2\frac{1}{5} = \frac{\overset{1}{\cancel{5}}}{4} \times \frac{11}{\cancel{5}} = \frac{11}{4} = 2\frac{3}{4}$

(b) $1\frac{1}{3} \div 1\frac{3}{5} = \frac{4}{3} \div \frac{8}{5} = \frac{\overset{1}{\cancel{4}}}{3} \times \frac{5}{\cancel{8}} = \frac{5}{6}$

The working can be simplified by dividing a numerator and a denominator by the same number.

Notice that dividing by $\frac{8}{5}$ is the same as multiplying by $\frac{5}{8}$.

● All fractions can be written as decimals.

To change a fraction to a decimal divide the **numerator** by the **denominator**.

Eg 4 Change $\frac{4}{5}$ to a decimal.
$\frac{4}{5} = 4 \div 5 = 0.8$

● Some decimals have **recurring digits**. These are shown by:

a single dot above a single recurring digit,

Eg 5 $\frac{2}{3} = 0.6666... = 0.\dot{6}$

a dot above the first and last digit of a set of recurring digits.

Eg 6 $\frac{5}{11} = 0.454545... = 0.\dot{4}\dot{5}$

Exercise 2

Do not use a calculator for questions 1 to 17.

1 (a) Lucy works out 0.2×0.4. She gets the answer 0.8. Explain why her answer must be wrong.
(b) Work out (i) 0.3×0.4, (ii) 0.3×0.2.

2 Paddy worked out that $\frac{30}{0.05} = 60$.

His friend did a quick mental calculation and told him he had made a mistake.
Show how Paddy's friend could have done this calculation mentally.

3 Work out. (a) $5 - 2.36$ (b) 4.8×2.5 (c) $0.294 \div 12$ (d) $\frac{54.4 \div 0.4}{0.2 \times 0.5}$

4 Two pieces of wood of length 0.75 m and 2.68 m are sawn from a plank 5 m long.
What length of wood is left?

5 Joseph did the following calculation: $28 \div 8.5 = 3.2$
(a) Write down the multiplication which Joseph could do to **check** his answer.
(b) Was Joseph's answer correct? Show your working.   Edexcel

6 $5 \times m$ gives an answer **less than 5**.
$5 \div m$ gives an answer **more than 5**.
Give two possible values for m which satisfy **both** conditions.

7 Ann wins £160. She gives $\frac{1}{4}$ of £160 to Pat, $\frac{3}{8}$ of £160 to John and £28 to Peter.
What fraction of the £160 does Ann keep? Give your fraction in its simplest form.   Edexcel

8 (a) Write down a fraction that lies halfway between $\frac{1}{3}$ and $\frac{1}{2}$.
(b) An examination is marked out of 48. Ashley scored 32 marks.
What fraction of the total did he score? Give your answer in its simplest form.

9 George pays £1.82 for $\frac{1}{5}$ kg of toffees at £4.20 per kilogram and $\frac{1}{4}$ kg of jellies.
How much per kilogram are jellies?

10 Work out. (a) $\frac{3}{5} \times \frac{1}{2}$ (b) $\frac{3}{4} - \frac{1}{3}$ (c) $1\frac{1}{2} + 2\frac{3}{5}$

11 (a) Change $\frac{1}{6}$ to a decimal. Give the answer correct to 3 d.p.
(b) Write these numbers in order of size, starting with the largest.

| 1.067 | 1.7 | 1.66 | $1\frac{1}{6}$ | 1.67 |

(c) Change 0.65 to a fraction in its simplest form.

12 Work out. (a) $4 - 1\frac{2}{3}$ (b) $\frac{3}{4} \times 1\frac{1}{5}$ (c) $4\frac{1}{2} \div \frac{3}{8}$

13 Which of the following fractions is nearest to $\frac{3}{4}$?

| $\frac{7}{10}$ | $\frac{2}{3}$ | $\frac{7}{8}$ | $\frac{9}{11}$ |

Show how you decide.

14 Work out. (a) $2\frac{2}{3} + 3\frac{3}{4}$ (b) $4\frac{3}{10} - 2\frac{1}{2}$ (c) $1\frac{3}{7} \times 2\frac{4}{5}$ (d) $2\frac{5}{6} \div 1\frac{2}{3}$

15 Income tax and national insurance take $\frac{1}{5}$ of Phillip's pay.
He gives $\frac{2}{5}$ of what he has left to his parents for housekeeping.
What fraction of his pay does Phillip have left for himself?

16 Three-fifths of the people at a party are boys. Three-quarters of the boys are wearing fancy dress.
What fraction of the people at the party are boys wearing fancy dress?

17 In a sale the price of a microwave is reduced by $\frac{1}{5}$. The sale price is £96.
What was the price of the microwave before the sale?

18 Work out. $\frac{12.9 \times 7.3}{3.9 + 1.4}$. Write down your full calculator display.

19 Use your calculator to work out the exact value of $\frac{14.82 \times (17.4 - 9.25)}{(54.3 + 23.7) \times 3.8}$ Edexcel

Approximation and Estimation

What you need to know

- How to **round** to the nearest 10, 100, 1000.

- How to approximate using **decimal places**.

  > Write the number using one more decimal place than asked for.
  > Look at the last decimal place and
  > - if the figure is 5 or more round up,
  > - if the figure is less than 5 round down.

  Eg 1 Write the number 3.649 to
  (a) 2 decimal places,
  (b) 1 decimal place.

  (a) 3.65
  (b) 3.6

- How to approximate using **significant figures**.

  > Start from the most significant figure and count the required number of figures.
  > Look at the next figure to the right of this and
  > - if the figure is 5 or more round up,
  > - if the figure is less than 5 round down.
  > Add noughts, as necessary, to locate the decimal point and preserve the place value.

  Eg 2 Write each of these numbers correct to 2 significant figures.
  (a) 365
  (b) 0.0423

  (a) 370
  (b) 0.042

- You should be able to choose a suitable degree of accuracy.

  > The result of a calculation involving measurement should not be given to a greater degree of accuracy than the measurements used in the calculation.

- Be able to use approximations to estimate that the actual answer to a calculation is of the right order of magnitude.

  Eg 3 Use approximations to estimate $\dfrac{5.1 \times 57.2}{9.8}$

  $\dfrac{5 \times 60}{10} = 30$

  > Estimation is done by approximating every number in the calculation to one significant figure.
  > The calculation is then done using the approximated values.

Exercise 3

Do not use a calculator for questions 1 to 12.

1 Write the result shown on the calculator display
(a) to the nearest whole number,
(b) to the nearest ten,
(c) to the nearest hundred,
(d) correct to one decimal place,
(e) correct to one significant figure.

626.47

2 A newspaper's headline states: "20 000 people attend concert".
The number in the newspaper is given to the nearest thousand.
What is the smallest possible attendance?

3 On Saturday a dairy sold 2975 litres of milk at 42 pence per litre.
By rounding each number to one significant figure, estimate the amount of money received from the sale of milk, giving your answer in pounds.

4 (a) Write down two numbers you could use to get an approximate answer to 41×89.
(b) Work out your approximate answer.
(c) Work out the difference between your approximate answer and the exact answer. Edexcel

5 (a) To estimate 97×49 Charlie uses the approximations 100×50.
Explain why his estimate will be larger than the actual answer.
(b) To estimate $1067 \div 48$ Patsy uses the approximations $1000 \div 50$.
Will her estimate be larger or smaller than the actual answer?
Give a reason for your answer.

6 A concert hall has 22 rows of seats. Each row has 69 seats.
(a) Work out an approximate answer to the total number of seats in the concert hall.

Every person attending a concert pays £9.75 on entry. Every seat in the concert hall is filled.
(b) Work out the approximate amount of money taken at the concert hall. Edexcel

7 Clint has to calculate $\dfrac{414 + 198}{36}$. He calculates the answer to be 419.5.

By rounding each number to one significant figure estimate whether his answer is about right.
Show all your working.

8 Explain how you can **estimate** the value of the following by approximating the three numbers
and give your approximate answer. $\dfrac{0.251 \times 81.376}{5.096}$ Edexcel

9 In 2001 Mr Symms drove 8873 kilometres.
His car does 11 kilometres per litre. Petrol costs 69.9 pence per litre.
Use approximations to estimate the amount he spent on petrol.

10 Melanie needs 200 crackers for an office party.
The crackers are sold in boxes of 12.
How many boxes must she buy?

11 Garth calculates $734\,990 \div 0.067$. He gets the answer $1\,097\,000$.
Use approximations to check whether his answer is of the right magnitude.

12 Use approximations to estimate the value of the following.
(a) $\dfrac{6.12}{11.3 + 19.8}$
(b) $\dfrac{0.613}{297}$
(c) $\dfrac{897 \times 5.03}{0.304}$

13 Calculate $97.2 \div 6.5$.
Give your answer correct to (a) two decimal places, (b) one decimal place.

14 Calculate 78.4×8.7.
Give your answer correct to (a) two significant figures, (b) one significant figure.

15 Comment on the difference between 9.9 and 9.90 as decimals. Edexcel

16 John made the statement:

> **"If you are given a number written correct to 2 decimal places it is more
> accurate than when written correct to 2 significant figures."**

John chose 6.60 and 6.6 as examples.
(a) Explain clearly how John could use these numbers to justify his statement.
(b) Is John's statement always true? Justify your answer. Edexcel

17 (a) Calculate $\dfrac{88.3 \times 4.24}{72.5 - 9.87}$.
(b) By using approximations show that your answer to (a) is about right.
You **must** show all your working. Edexcel

Approximation and Estimation

Percentages and Money ●●●

What you need to know

- 10% is read as '10 percent'.   'Per cent' means out of 100.   10% means 10 out of 100.

- A percentage can be written as a fraction, 10% can be written as $\frac{10}{100}$.

- To change a decimal or a fraction to a percentage: **multiply by 100**.

- To change a percentage to a fraction or a decimal: **divide by 100**.

- How to express one quantity as a percentage of another.

  Eg 1   Write 30p as a percentage of £2.

  $\frac{30}{200} \times 100 = 30 \times 100 \div 200 = 15\%$

  > Write the numbers as a fraction, using the same units.
  > Change the fraction to a percentage.

- You should be able to use percentages to solve a variety of problems.

- Be able to find a percentage of a quantity.

  Eg 2   Find 20% of £64.
  £64 ÷ 100 = £0.64
  £0.64 × 20 = £12.80

  > 1. Divide by 100 to find 1%.
  > 2. Multiply by the percentage to be found.

- Be able to find a percentage increase (or decrease).

  Eg 3   Find the percentage loss on a micro-scooter bought for £25 and sold for £18.

  Percentage loss = $\frac{7}{25} \times 100 = 28\%$

  > Percentage decrease = $\dfrac{\text{actual decrease}}{\text{initial value}} \times 100\%$
  >
  > Percentage increase = $\dfrac{\text{actual increase}}{\text{initial value}} \times 100\%$

- Be able to solve reverse percentage problems.

  Eg 4   Find the original price of a car which is sold at a loss of 20% for £1200.

  80% of original price = £1200
   1% of original price = £1200 ÷ 80 = £15
      Original price = £15 × 100 = £1500

  > First find 1% of the original value by dividing the selling price by (100 − % loss), then multiply by 100.

- **Hourly pay** is paid at a **basic rate** for a fixed number of hours.
  Overtime pay is usually paid at a higher rate such as time and a half, which means each hour's work is worth 1.5 times the basic rate.

- Everyone is allowed to earn some money which is not taxed. This is called a **tax allowance**.

- Tax is only paid on income earned in excess of the tax allowance. This is called **taxable income**.

  Eg 5   Tom earns £5800 per year. His tax allowance is £4615 per year and he pays tax at 10p in the £ on his taxable income. Find how much income tax Tom pays per year.

  Taxable income   = £5800 − £4615 = £1185
  Income tax payable = £1185 × 0.10   = £118.50

  > First find the taxable income, then multiply taxable income by rate in £.

- **Value added tax**, or **VAT**, is a tax on some goods and services and is added to the bill.

- When considering a **best buy**, compare quantities by using the same units.
  For example, find which product gives more grams per penny.

- Money invested in a savings account at a bank or building society earns **interest**.

- With **Simple Interest**, the interest is paid out each year and not added to your account.

$$\text{Simple Interest} = \frac{\text{Amount}}{\text{invested}} \times \frac{\text{Time in}}{\text{years}} \times \frac{\text{Rate of interest}}{\text{per year}}$$

Eg 6 Find the Simple Interest paid on £600 invested for 6 months at 8% per year.

Simple Interest $= 600 \times \frac{6}{12} \times \frac{8}{100} = 600 \times 0.5 \times 0.08 = £24$

- With **Compound Interest**, the interest earned each year is added to your account and also earns interest the following year.

Eg 7 Find the **Compound Interest** paid on £600 invested for 2 years at 6% per year.

1st year		**2nd year**	
Investment	= £600	Investment	= £636
Interest: £600 × 0.06	= £ 36	Interest: £636 × 0.06	= £ 38.16
Value after one year	= £636	Value after two years	= £674.16

Compound Interest = Final value − Original value = £674.16 − £600 = £74.16

Exercise 4   Do not use a calculator for questions 1 to 5.

1. (a) Work out (i) 25% of 60 kg,   (ii) 5% of £900.
   (b) What is (i) 60 pence as a percentage of £3, (ii) 15 seconds as a percentage of 1 minute?

2. A test is marked out of 80. Colin scored 35% of the marks.
   How many marks did Colin score?

3. A jacket normally costs £48. The price is reduced by 15% in a sale.
   What is the price of the jacket in the sale?

4. Angela is paid £7.40 per hour for a basic 35-hour week. Overtime is paid at time and a half.
   Last week Angela was paid £303.40.
   How many hours did she work last week?

5. Mrs Tilsed wishes to buy a car priced at £2400.

   > **Two options are available.**
   > **Option 1** – A deposit of 20% of £2400 and 24 monthly payments of £95.
   > **Option 2** – For a single payment the dealer offers a discount of 5% on £2400.

   £2400

   How much more does it cost to buy the car if option 1 is chosen rather than option 2?

6. Asif sells computers.
   Each week Asif is paid £150 plus £20.50 for each computer he sells that week.
   Last week Asif was paid £888.
   (a) Work out how many computers Asif sold last week.

   Jane is going to buy a computer for £480 + $17\frac{1}{2}$% VAT.
   (b) Work out the total price, including VAT, that Jane will pay for the computer.   Edexcel

7. A pogo stick is bought for £12.50 and sold for £8. What is the percentage loss?

8. Toffee is sold in bars of two sizes.
   A large bar weighs 450 g and costs £1.69. A small bar weighs 275 g and costs 99p.
   Which size of bar is better value for money? You must show all your working.

9 A farmer has 200 sheep. 90% of the sheep have lambs.
Of the sheep which have lambs 45% have two lambs.
How many of the sheep have two lambs?

10 Lily invests £1000 at 4.25% per annum simple interest.
She withdraws her money after 6 months.
How much interest did she get?

11 Last year Leroy had a tax allowance of £4615 and paid £3778 in tax.
How much did Leroy earn last year if he paid tax at the rate of 10p in the £ on the first £1920
of his taxable income and 22p in the £ on all his remaining income?

12 Shreena put £484 in a new savings account.
At the end of every year, interest of 4.3% was added to the amount in her savings account at
the start of that year.
Calculate the total amount in Shreena's savings account at the end of 2 years. *Edexcel*

13

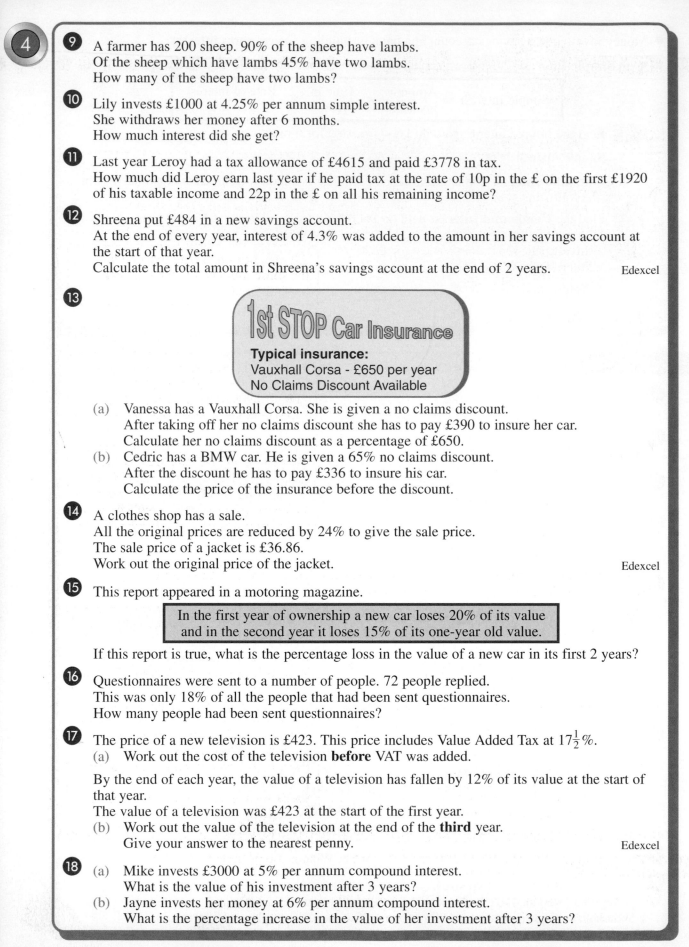

1st STOP Car Insurance

Typical insurance:
Vauxhall Corsa - £650 per year
No Claims Discount Available

(a) Vanessa has a Vauxhall Corsa. She is given a no claims discount.
After taking off her no claims discount she has to pay £390 to insure her car.
Calculate her no claims discount as a percentage of £650.

(b) Cedric has a BMW car. He is given a 65% no claims discount.
After the discount he has to pay £336 to insure his car.
Calculate the price of the insurance before the discount.

14 A clothes shop has a sale.
All the original prices are reduced by 24% to give the sale price.
The sale price of a jacket is £36.86.
Work out the original price of the jacket. *Edexcel*

15 This report appeared in a motoring magazine.

> In the first year of ownership a new car loses 20% of its value
> and in the second year it loses 15% of its one-year old value.

If this report is true, what is the percentage loss in the value of a new car in its first 2 years?

16 Questionnaires were sent to a number of people. 72 people replied.
This was only 18% of all the people that had been sent questionnaires.
How many people had been sent questionnaires?

17 The price of a new television is £423. This price includes Value Added Tax at $17\frac{1}{2}$%.
(a) Work out the cost of the television **before** VAT was added.

By the end of each year, the value of a television has fallen by 12% of its value at the start of
that year.
The value of a television was £423 at the start of the first year.
(b) Work out the value of the television at the end of the **third** year.
Give your answer to the nearest penny. *Edexcel*

18 (a) Mike invests £3000 at 5% per annum compound interest.
What is the value of his investment after 3 years?
(b) Jayne invests her money at 6% per annum compound interest.
What is the percentage increase in the value of her investment after 3 years?

What you need to know

● The ratio 3 : 2 is read '3 to 2'.

● A ratio is used only to **compare** quantities.
A ratio does not give information about the exact values of quantities being compared.

● In its **simplest form**, a ratio contains whole numbers which have no common factor other than 1.

Eg 1 Write £2.40 : 40p in its simplest form.
£2.40 : 40p = 240p : 40p
= 240 : 40
= 6 : 1

> All quantities in a ratio must be in the **same units** before the ratio can be simplified.

● You should be able to solve a variety of problems involving ratio.

Eg 2 The ratio of bats to balls in a box is 3 : 5.
There are 12 bats in the box.
How many balls are there?

12 ÷ 3 = 4
3 × 4 : 5 × 4 = 12 : 20
There are 20 balls in the box.

> For every 3 bats there are 5 balls.
> To find an **equivalent ratio** to 3 : 5, in which the first number is 12, multiply each number in the ratio by 4.

Eg 3 A wall costs £660 to build.
The costs of materials to labour are in the ratio 4 : 7.
What is the cost of labour?

4 + 7 = 11
£660 ÷ 11 = £60
Cost of labour = £60 × 7 = £420

> The numbers in the ratio add to 11.
> For every £11 of the total cost, £4 pays for materials and £7 pays for labour.
> So, **divide** by 11 and then **multiply** by 7.

● When two different quantities are always in the **same ratio** the two quantities are in **direct proportion**.

Eg 4 20 litres of petrol cost £14.
Find the cost of 25 litres of petrol.

20 litres cost £14
1 litre costs £14 ÷ 20 = £0.70
25 litres cost £0.70 × 25 = £17.50

> This is sometimes called the **unitary method**.
> **Divide** by 20 to find the cost of 1 litre.
> **Multiply** by 25 to find the cost of 25 litres.

● When as one quantity increases the other decreases, the quantities are in **inverse proportion**.

Eg 5 3 people take 8 hours to deliver some leaflets.
How long would it take 4 people?

3 people take 8 hours.
1 person takes 8 hours × 3 = 24 hours
4 people take 24 hours ÷ 4 = 6 hours
So 4 people would take 6 hours.

> This assumes that time is **inversely proportional** to the number of people.
> **Multiply** by 3 to find how long 1 person would take.
> **Divide** by 4 to find how long 4 people would take.

Exercise 5   Do not use a calculator for questions 1 to 6.

1   A toy box contains large bricks and small bricks in the ratio 1 : 4.
The box contains 40 bricks. How many large bricks are in the box?

5

2 To make mortar a builder mixes sand and cement in the ratio 3 : 1.
The builder uses 2.5 kg of cement. How much sand does he use?

3 In a drama club the ratio of boys to girls is 2 : 3.
(a) What fraction of club members are girls?
(b) What percentage of club members are boys?

4 The ratio of men to women playing golf one day is 5 : 3.
There are 20 men playing. How many women are playing?

5 Rashid has 35 sweets.
He shares them in the ratio 4 : 3 with his sister.
Rashid keeps the larger share.
How many sweets does Rashid keep?

Edexcel

6 Dec shares a prize of £435 with Annabel in the ratio 3 : 2.
What is the difference in the amount of money they each receive?

7 To make 20 m³ of concrete for a building, the builders use:

4 m³ of cement, 12 m³ of sand and 4 m³ of ballast.

(a) What is the ratio of cement to sand? Give your answer in its lowest terms.
(b) How much cement would be needed for 100 m³ of concrete?

Edexcel

8 A bag contains red counters and white counters in the ratio 3 : 5.
Six red counters are taken from the bag.
The ratio of red counters to white counters left in the bag is 1 : 5.
How many counters are left in the bag?

9 Two students are talking about their school outing.

My class went to Tower Bridge last week.
There are 30 people in my class.
The total cost was £82.50

There are 45 people in my group.
What will be the total cost for my group?

10 Three 1-litre tins of paint cost a total of £26.85.
Find the cost of five of the 1-litre tins of paint.

Edexcel

11 A farmer estimates it will take 2 combine harvesters 6 days to harvest his crop.
Estimate how many days it will take 3 combine harvesters to harvest his crop.

12 When petrol is 70 pence a litre it costs £24.50 to fill the tank of my car with petrol.
How much will it cost to fill the tank of my car with petrol when petrol is 80 pence per litre?

13 On a map the distance between two towns is 5 cm.
The actual distance between the towns is 1 kilometre.
What is the scale of the map in the form of 1 : n?

14 Malika's father won £128.
He shared the £128 between his three children in the ratio 6 : 3 : 1.
(a) Malika was given the biggest share. Work out how much money Malika received.
(b) Malika saved $\frac{2}{3}$ of her share. Work out how much Malika saved.

Edexcel

15 At 80 km/h it takes 30 minutes to complete a journey.
How long would it take to complete the journey at 50 km/h?

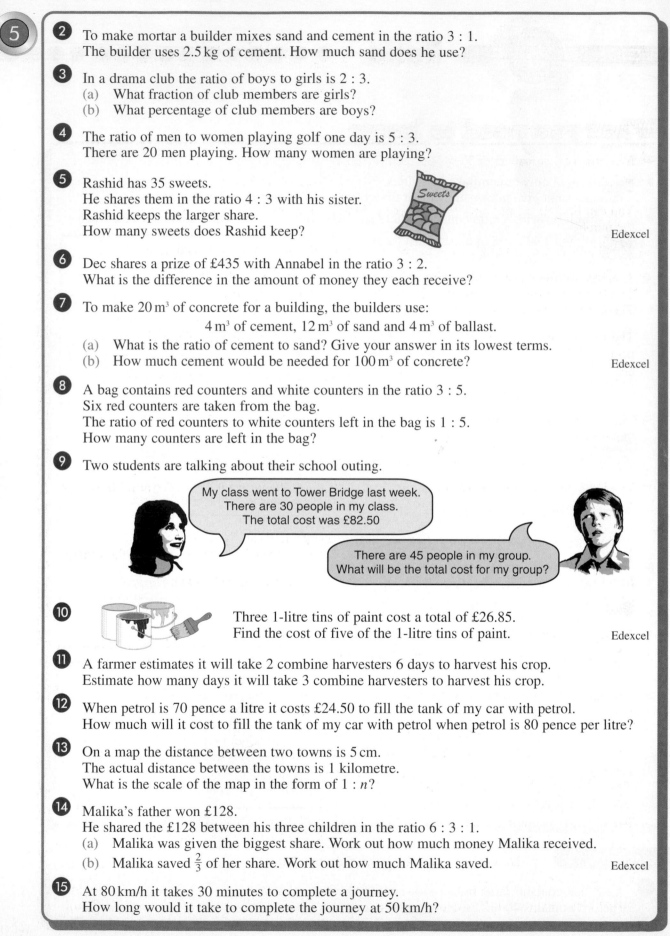

Working with Number •••••

What you need to know

- **Multiples** of a number are found by multiplying the number by 1, 2, 3, 4, …

  Eg 1 The multiples of 8 are $1 \times 8 = 8$, $2 \times 8 = 16$, $3 \times 8 = 24$, $4 \times 8 = 32$, …

- You can find **all** the **factors** of a number by finding all the multiplication facts that give the number.

  Eg 2 $1 \times 6 = 6$ and $2 \times 3 = 6$. So, the factors of 6 are: 1, 2, 3 and 6.

- A **prime number** is a number with only two factors, 1 and the number itself.
  The first few prime numbers are: 2, 3, 5, 7, 11, 13, 17, 19, …
  The number 1 is not a prime number because it has only one factor.

- The **prime factors** of a number are those factors of the number which are themselves prime numbers.

  Eg 3 The factors of 18 are: 1, 2, 3, 6, 9 and 18.
  The prime factors of 18 are: 2 and 3.

- The **Least Common Multiple** of two numbers is the smallest number that is a multiple of them both.

  Eg 4 The Least Common Multiple of 4 and 5 is 20.

- The **Highest Common Factor** of two numbers is the largest number that is a factor of them both.

  Eg 5 The Highest Common Factor of 8 and 12 is 4.

- An expression such as $3 \times 3 \times 3 \times 3 \times 3$ can be written in a shorthand way as 3^5.
  This is read as '3 to the power of 5'. The number 3 is the **base** of the expression. 5 is the **power**.

- Powers can be used to help write any number as the **product of its prime factors**.

  Eg 6 $72 = 2 \times 2 \times 2 \times 3 \times 3 = 2^3 \times 3^2$

- Numbers raised to the power of 2 are **squared**.

  Squares can be calculated using the $\boxed{x^2}$ button on a calculator.

  The opposite of squaring a number is called finding the **square root**.

  Square roots can be calculated using the $\boxed{\sqrt{}}$ button on a calculator.

  The square root of a number can be positive or negative.

  > **Square numbers** are whole numbers squared.
  > The first few square numbers are:
  > 1, 4, 9, 16, 25, 36, …

  Eg 7 The square root of 9 can be written as $\sqrt{9}$ or $9^{\frac{1}{2}}$, and is equal to $+3$ or -3.

- Numbers raised to the power of 3 are **cubed**.
  The opposite of cubing a number is called finding the **cube root**.

  Cube roots can be calculated using the $\boxed{\sqrt[3]{}}$ button on a calculator.

  > **Cube numbers** are whole numbers cubed.
  > The first few cube numbers are:
  > 1, 8, 27, 64, 125, …

  Eg 8 The cube root of 27 can be written as $\sqrt[3]{27}$ or $27^{\frac{1}{3}}$, and is equal to 3.

- **Powers**

The squares and cubes of numbers can be worked out on a calculator by using the $\boxed{x^y}$ button.
The $\boxed{x^y}$ button can be used to calculate the value of a number x raised to the power of y.

Eg 9 Calculate 2.6^4.
Enter the sequence: $\boxed{2}$ $\boxed{.}$ $\boxed{6}$ $\boxed{x^y}$ $\boxed{4}$ $\boxed{=}$. So $2.6^4 = 45.6976$.

- The **reciprocal** of a number is the value obtained when the number is divided into 1.
The reciprocal of a number can be found on a calculator by using the $\boxed{\frac{1}{x}}$ button.

> A number times its reciprocal equals 1.
> Zero has no reciprocal.
> The reciprocal of a number can be shown using an index of -1.

Eg 10 Find the reciprocal of 5.
The reciprocal of $5 = 5^{-1} = \frac{1}{5} = 0.2$
Using a calculator, press: $\boxed{5}$ $\boxed{\frac{1}{x}}$

- **Roots** can be calculated using the $\boxed{x^{1/y}}$ button.

Eg 11 Calculate $\sqrt[7]{128}$.
Enter the sequence: $\boxed{1}$ $\boxed{2}$ $\boxed{8}$ $\boxed{x^{1/y}}$ $\boxed{7}$ $\boxed{=}$. So $\sqrt[7]{128} = 2$.

- **The rules of indices**

Multiplying powers with the same base	$a^m \times a^n = a^{m+n}$
Dividing powers with the same base	$a^m \div a^n = a^{m-n}$
Raising a power to a power	$(a^m)^n = a^{mn}$
Raising any number to the power zero	$a^0 = 1$ (also $a^1 = a$)
Negative powers and reciprocals	$a^{-m} = \dfrac{1}{a^m}$ $\quad$ a^{-m} is the reciprocal of a^m
Fractional powers and roots	$a^{\frac{1}{n}} = \sqrt[n]{a}$ and $a^{\frac{m}{n}} = \left(a^{\frac{1}{n}}\right)^m = \left(\sqrt[n]{a}\right)^m$

Eg 12 Simplify. Leave your answers in index form.
(a) $2^9 \times 2^4 = 2^{9+4} = 2^{13}$ (b) $2^9 \div 2^4 = 2^{9-4} = 2^5$ (c) $(4^9)^3 = 4^{9 \times 3} = 4^{27}$

- You should be able to use the function keys on a calculator to solve a variety of problems.

Exercise 6   Do not use a calculator for questions 1 to 17.

1 (a) Write down all the factors of 18.
   (b) Write down a multiple of 7 between 30 and 40.
   (c) Explain why 15 is not a prime number.

2 A number of counters can be grouped into 2's, 3's, 4's and 5's.
Find the smallest possible number of counters.

3 Look at these numbers. | 2   15   27   36   44   51   64 |
   (a) Which of these numbers is a prime number?
   (b) Which of these numbers is both a square number and a cube number?

4 Use examples to show that the sum of the squares of two prime numbers can be odd or even.

5 Find the value of $\sqrt{(2 \times 2 \times 3 \times 3 \times 5 \times 5)}$ Edexcel

6 (a) Write 36 as a product of its prime factors.
   (b) Write 45 as a product of its prime factors.
   (c) What is the highest common factor of 36 and 45?
   (d) What is the least common multiple of 36 and 45?

7 Work out.   (a) $2^3 \times 3^2$ (b) $\left(\sqrt{9} \times \sqrt{25}\right)^2$ (c) $2^3 \times \sqrt[3]{64}$

8 A white light flashes every 10 seconds. A red light flashes every 6 seconds.
The two lights flash at the same time.
After how many seconds will the lights next flash at the same time?

9 (a) Which is smaller $\sqrt{225}$ or 2^4? Show your working.
(b) Work out the value of $3^1 - 3^0 + 3^{-1}$.

10 Find the value of x in each of the following.
(a) $7^6 \times 7^3 = 7^x$ (b) $7^6 \div 7^3 = 7^x$ (c) $(7^6)^3 = 7^x$ (d) $7^0 = x$

11 Simplify fully each of these expressions. Leave your answers in power form.
(a) $3^2 \times 3^3$ (b) $4^{-2} \times 4^5$ (c) $5^6 \div 5^3$ (d) $9^4 \div 9^{-2}$ (e) $\dfrac{2^3 \times 2}{2^6}$

12 Which is bigger 2^3 or the reciprocal of 0.1? Show your working.

13 Find the value of n when: (a) $10^3 \times 10^{-5} = 10^n$
(b) $(4 \times 10^5) \times (5 \times 10^{-3}) = 2 \times 10^n$
(c) $(4 \times 10^5) \div (5 \times 10^{-3}) = 8 \times 10^n$

14 $y = 2^{-x}$ Calculate the value of y when   (a) $x = 0$,   (b) $x = 3$.   *Edexcel*

15 Evaluate: (a) $9^{\frac{1}{2}}$ (b) $64^{-\frac{1}{2}}$ (c) $25^{\frac{3}{2}}$ (d) $16^{-\frac{3}{4}}$ (e) $32^{\frac{1}{5}}$

16 Simplify, leaving your answers in fractional form.
(a) $64^{\frac{1}{2}} \times 125^{-\frac{1}{3}}$ (b) $27^{\frac{2}{3}} \times 3^{-4}$ (c) $\left(\frac{1}{2}\right)^{-3} \div \left(\frac{1}{5}\right)^{-2}$

17 The number x lies between 0 and 1.
(a) Write the following five expressions in order of size.
Put the smallest one first.

$$x^2 \qquad \sqrt{x} \qquad x^3 \qquad \frac{1}{\sqrt{x}} \qquad x$$

The number x and the number y both lie between 0 and 1.
(b) For which of the following expressions could the value be greater than 1?

$$xy \qquad xy^2 \qquad (xy)^2 \qquad \frac{x}{y} \qquad \sqrt{\left(\frac{x}{y}\right)}$$

Edexcel

18 Find the reciprocal of 7. Give your answer correct to two decimal places.

19 (a) Use your calculator to find the value of $5.43 \times \sqrt{(18 - 6.67)}$.
Write down all the figures on your calculator display.
(b) Give your answer to part (a) correct to 2 decimal places.   *Edexcel*

20 Use your calculator to find the value of $\sqrt{47.3^2 - 9.1^2}$).
(a) Write down all the figures on your calculator display.
(b) Write your answer to part (a) correct to 2 significant figures.   *Edexcel*

21 Use your calculator to work out the value of $\dfrac{\sqrt{12.3^2 + 7.9}}{1.8 \times 0.17}$
Give your answer correct to 1 decimal place.   *Edexcel*

22 (a) Calculate the value of $\sqrt{\dfrac{4.1}{(0.19)^3}}$
(b) Show how to check that your answer is of the right order of magnitude.

23 Calculate the value of:
(a) $5^{\frac{2}{5}}$ (b) $\dfrac{1}{(0.7)^5}$ (c) $\sqrt[3]{\dfrac{920\,000}{5^4}}$ (d) $\left(\dfrac{5.9}{\sqrt[5]{15}}\right)^{-3}$

Give your answers correct to two significant figures.

Standard Index Form

What you need to know

- **Standard index form**, or **standard form**, is a shorthand way of writing very large and very small numbers.

- In **standard form** a number is written as: **a number between 1 and 10 × a power of 10**
  Large numbers (ten, or more) have a **positive** power of 10.

  Eg 1 Write 370 000 in standard form.
  $370\,000 = 3.7 \times 100\,000 = 3.7 \times 10^5$

  Eg 2 Write 5.6×10^7 as an ordinary number.
  $5.6 \times 10^7 = 5.6 \times 10\,000\,000 = 56\,000\,000$

  Small positive numbers (less than one) have a **negative** power of 10.

  Eg 3 Write 0.000 73 in standard form.
  $0.000\,73 = 7.3 \times 0.000\,1 = 7.3 \times 10^{-4}$

  Eg 4 Write 2.9×10^{-6} as an ordinary number.
  $2.9 \times 10^{-6} = 2.9 \times 0.000\,001 = 0.000\,002\,9$

- You should be able to interpret the display on a calculator.

  Eg 5 The calculator display shows the answer to 0.007×0.09
  In standard form, the answer is 6.3×10^{-4}
  As an ordinary number, the answer is 0.000 63

6.3	−04

- You should be able to solve problems involving numbers given in standard form.

Exercise 7

Do not use a calculator for questions 1 to 8.

1 Write one million in standard form.

2 Look at these numbers.

2.6×10^4	6.2×10^3	9.8×10^{-4}	8.9×10^{-5}

(a) (i) Which number is the largest?   (ii) Write your answer as an ordinary number.
(b) (i) Which number is the smallest?   (ii) Write your answer as an ordinary number.

3 (a) Write 57 000 000 in standard index form.
(b) Write 0.000 057 in standard index form.

4 Work out.
(a) $(6 \times 10^3) + (5 \times 10^4)$ (b) $(6 \times 10^3) \times (5 \times 10^4)$ (c) $(6 \times 10^3) \div (5 \times 10^4)$
Give your answers in standard form.

5 Work out $4 \times 10^8 - 4 \times 10^6$.
Give your answer in standard form.

Edexcel

6 The mass of an atom of oxygen is 0.000 000 000 000 000 000 000 027 grams.
(a) Write this number in standard form.
(b) Calculate, in standard form, the mass of 5×10^8 atoms of oxygen.

Edexcel

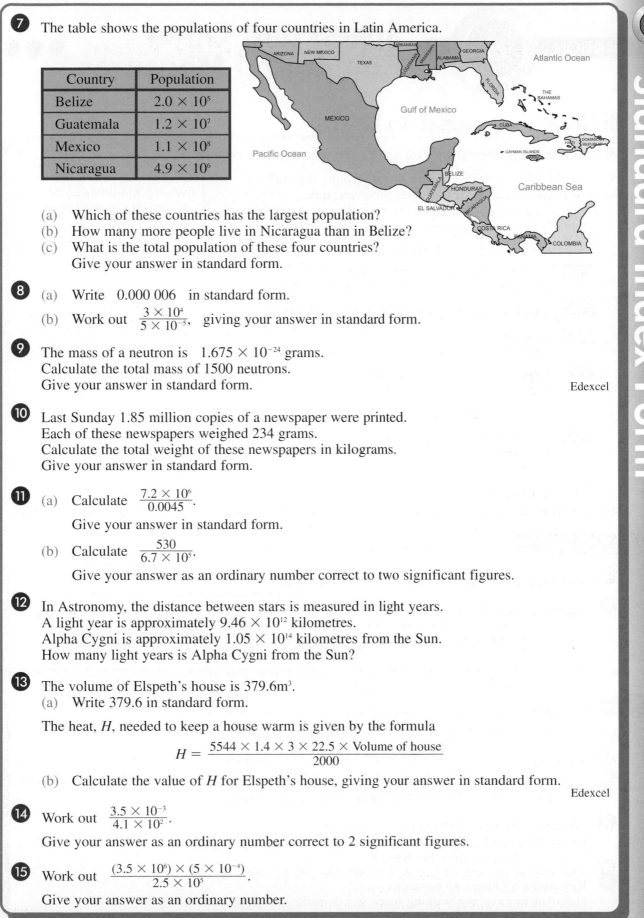

7 The table shows the populations of four countries in Latin America.

Country	Population
Belize	2.0×10^5
Guatemala	1.2×10^7
Mexico	1.1×10^8
Nicaragua	4.9×10^6

(a) Which of these countries has the largest population?
(b) How many more people live in Nicaragua than in Belize?
(c) What is the total population of these four countries?
    Give your answer in standard form.

8 (a) Write 0.000 006 in standard form.

(b) Work out $\dfrac{3 \times 10^4}{5 \times 10^{-5}}$, giving your answer in standard form.

9 The mass of a neutron is 1.675×10^{-24} grams.
Calculate the total mass of 1500 neutrons.
Give your answer in standard form.

Edexcel

10 Last Sunday 1.85 million copies of a newspaper were printed.
Each of these newspapers weighed 234 grams.
Calculate the total weight of these newspapers in kilograms.
Give your answer in standard form.

11 (a) Calculate $\dfrac{7.2 \times 10^6}{0.0045}$.

   Give your answer in standard form.

(b) Calculate $\dfrac{530}{6.7 \times 10^5}$.

   Give your answer as an ordinary number correct to two significant figures.

12 In Astronomy, the distance between stars is measured in light years.
A light year is approximately 9.46×10^{12} kilometres.
Alpha Cygni is approximately 1.05×10^{14} kilometres from the Sun.
How many light years is Alpha Cygni from the Sun?

13 The volume of Elspeth's house is 379.6m³.
(a) Write 379.6 in standard form.

The heat, H, needed to keep a house warm is given by the formula

$$H = \frac{5544 \times 1.4 \times 3 \times 22.5 \times \text{Volume of house}}{2000}$$

(b) Calculate the value of H for Elspeth's house, giving your answer in standard form.

Edexcel

14 Work out $\dfrac{3.5 \times 10^{-3}}{4.1 \times 10^2}$.

Give your answer as an ordinary number correct to 2 significant figures.

15 Work out $\dfrac{(3.5 \times 10^6) \times (5 \times 10^{-4})}{2.5 \times 10^5}$.

Give your answer as an ordinary number.

Speed and Other Compound Measures

What you need to know

- **Speed** is a compound measure because it involves **two** other measures.

- **Speed** is a measurement of how fast something is travelling.
  It involves two other measures, **distance** and **time**.
  In situations where speed is not constant, **average speed** is used.

  The formula linking speed, distance and time can be rearranged and remembered as:
  $$S = D \div T$$
  $$D = S \times T$$
  $$T = D \div S$$

$$\text{Speed} = \frac{\text{Distance}}{\text{Time}}$$

$$\text{Average speed} = \frac{\text{Total distance travelled}}{\text{Total time taken}}$$

- You should be able to solve problems involving speed, distance and time.

  Eg 1 A greyhound takes 32 seconds to run 400 metres.
  Calculate its speed in metres per second.

  $$\text{Speed} = \frac{\text{Distance}}{\text{Time}} = \frac{400}{32} = 12.5 \text{ metres per second}$$

  Eg 2 Norrie says, "If I drive at an average speed of 60 km/h it will take me $2\frac{1}{2}$ hours to complete my journey." What distance is his journey?

  $$\text{Distance} = \text{Speed} \times \text{Time} = 60 \times 2\frac{1}{2} = 150 \text{ km}$$

  Eg 3 Ellen cycles 5 km at an average speed of 12 km/h.
  How many minutes does she take?

  To change hours to minutes: **multiply by 60**

  $$\text{Time} = \frac{\text{Distance}}{\text{Speed}} = \frac{5}{12} \text{ hours} = \frac{5}{12} \times 60 = 25 \text{ minutes}$$

- **Density** is a compound measure which involves the measures **mass** and **volume**.

  Eg 4 A block of metal has mass 500 g and volume 400 cm³.

  $$\text{Density} = \frac{\text{Mass}}{\text{Volume}} = \frac{500}{400} = 1.25 \text{ g/cm}^3$$

  $$\text{Density} = \frac{\text{Mass}}{\text{Volume}}$$

- **Population density** is a measure of how populated an area is.

  Eg 5 The population of Cumbria is 489 700.
  The area of Cumbria is 6824 km².

  $$\text{Population density} = \frac{\text{Population}}{\text{Area}}$$

  $$\text{Population density} = \frac{\text{Population}}{\text{Area}} = \frac{489\,700}{6824} = 71.8 \text{ people/km}^2.$$

Exercise 8

Do not use a calculator for questions 1 to 4.

1. Marcus cycled 18 km at an average speed of 15 km/h.
   How long did he take to complete the journey? Give your answer in hours and minutes.

2. A motorist travels a distance of 156 miles in $3\frac{1}{4}$ hours.
   Calculate the average speed of the motorist in miles per hour.

3. Gail leaves home at 0950 to walk to the park.
   She walks at an average speed of 5 km/h and reaches the park at 1020.
   How far is the park from her home?

4. Kay walks 2.7 km in 45 minutes.
   Calculate her average walking speed in kilometres per hour.

5 In the College Games, Michael Jackson won the 200 metres race in a time of 20.32 seconds.
Calculate his average speed in metres per second.
Give your answer correct to 1 decimal place.

Edexcel

6 The diagram shows the distances, in miles, between some junctions on a motorway.

West ← 25 ——— **12** ——— 26 ——— **8** ——— 27 → East

A coach is travelling west. At 1040 it passes junction 27 and at 1052 it passes junction 26.
(a) Calculate the average speed of the coach in miles per hour.

Between junctions 26 and 25 the coach travels at an average speed of 30 miles per hour.
(b) Calculate the time when the coach passes junction 25.

7 A train travels at an average speed of 80 miles per hour.
At 0940 the train is 65 miles from Glasgow. The train is due to arrive in Glasgow at 1030.
Will it arrive on time? Show your working.

8 A horse gallops at an average speed of 24 km/h for $4\frac{1}{2}$ minutes.
Calculate the distance it travels.

9 On Monday it took Helen 40 minutes to drive to work.
On Tuesday it took Helen 25 minutes to drive to work.
Her average speed on Monday was 18 miles per hour.
What was her average speed on Tuesday?

10 Rhys completed a 400 m race in 64 seconds.
Calculate his average speed in kilometres per hour.

11 A jet-ski travels 0.9 kilometres in 1.5 minutes.
Calculate the average speed of the jet-ski in metres per second.

12 The distance from the Earth to the Moon is 3.81×10^5 kilometres.
Light travels at a speed of 3×10^8 metres per second.
How long does it take light to travel from the Earth to the Moon?

13 (a) A goods train, 150 metres long, is travelling at 45 km/h.
How many seconds does it take to pass a signal?
(b) The goods train takes 5 seconds to pass a passenger train, 90 metres long,
travelling in the opposite direction.
Calculate the speed of the passenger train in kilometres per hour.

14 A copper statue has a mass of 1080 g and a volume of 120 cm³.
Work out the density of copper.

15 A silver medal has a mass of 200 g. The density of silver is 10.5 g/cm³.
What is the volume of the medal?

16 The population of Jamaica is 2.8 million people. The area of Jamaica is 10 800 km².
What is the population density of Jamaica?

17 The table gives some information about North America.

Country	Area (km²)	Population	Population density (people/km²)
Canada	9 860 000		2.98
United States		2.68×10^8	28.9

(a) Calculate the population of Canada.
(b) Calculate the area of the United States.
Give your answers to 3 significant figures.

Speed and Other Compound Measures

Extending the Number System

What you need to know

- **Rational numbers** can be written in the form $\frac{a}{b}$, where a and b are integers ($b \neq 0$).

  Examples of rational numbers are: 2, -5, $\frac{2}{5}$,   0.6,   3.47, $1\frac{3}{4}$.

- All fractions can be written as decimals.
  For example, $\frac{1}{3} = 0.3333333\ldots = 0.\dot{3}$, $\frac{123}{999} = 0.123123123\ldots = 0.\dot{1}2\dot{3}$

- You should be able to convert a recurring decimal to a fraction.

  Eg 1 Find the fraction which is equal to $0.\dot{2}\dot{7}$, in its simplest form.

  $x = 0.2727\ldots$
  2 digits recur, so multiply by 100.
  $100x = 27.2727\ldots$
  $99x = 27$
  $x = \frac{27}{99} = \frac{3}{11}$
  $0.\dot{2}\dot{7} = \frac{3}{11}$

  Let $x =$ the recurring decimal.
  Multiply both sides by a power of 10:
  - by $10^1 = 10$ if only 1 digit recurs,
  - by $10^2 = 100$ if 2 digits recur, and so on.

  Subtract the original equation from the new equation.
  Solve the resulting equation for x.
  If necessary, write the fraction in its simplest form.

- All **terminating** and **recurring decimals** are rational numbers.

- A **surd** is the root of a rational number which is not rational.
  A surd is an **irrational number**.

  These are examples of surds: $\sqrt{2}$ $\sqrt{0.37}$ $3 + \sqrt{2}$

  $\sqrt{9}$ is not a surd because $\sqrt{9} = 3$ which is rational. | $\sqrt{a}$ means the positive square root of a. |

- Rules for manipulating and simplifying surds:

  $$\sqrt{ab} = \sqrt{a} \times \sqrt{b} \qquad m\sqrt{a} + n\sqrt{a} = (m + n)\sqrt{a} \qquad \sqrt{\frac{a}{b}} = \frac{\sqrt{a}}{\sqrt{b}}$$

  Eg 2 Simplify the following leaving the answers in surd form.

  (a) $\sqrt{32} = \sqrt{16} \times \sqrt{2} = 4\sqrt{2}$ | Look for factors that are square numbers. |

  (b) $\sqrt{8} + \sqrt{18} = \sqrt{4} \times \sqrt{2} + \sqrt{9} \times \sqrt{2} = 2\sqrt{2} + 3\sqrt{2} = 5\sqrt{2}$

  (c) $\sqrt{\frac{72}{20}} = \frac{\sqrt{72}}{\sqrt{20}} = \frac{\sqrt{36}\,\sqrt{2}}{\sqrt{4}\,\sqrt{5}} = \frac{6\,\sqrt{2}}{2\,\sqrt{5}} = \frac{3\,\sqrt{2}}{\sqrt{5}}$

- To **rationalise** the denominator of a fraction of the form $\frac{a}{\sqrt{b}}$ multiply both the numerator (top) and the denominator (bottom) of the fraction by $\sqrt{b}$.

  Eg 3 Rationalise the denominator and simplify where possible: $\frac{3\,\sqrt{2}}{\sqrt{6}}$.

  $$\frac{3\,\sqrt{2}}{\sqrt{6}} = \frac{3\,\sqrt{2}}{\sqrt{6}} \times \frac{\sqrt{6}}{\sqrt{6}} = \frac{3\,\sqrt{2}\,\sqrt{6}}{6} = \frac{3\,\sqrt{2}\,\sqrt{2}\,\sqrt{3}}{6} = \frac{6\,\sqrt{3}}{6} = \sqrt{3}$$

- You should be able to use surds in calculations.

  | To keep an answer exact it is necessary to keep numbers like $\sqrt{3}$ in surd form. |

1 (a) Change $\frac{5}{7}$ into a decimal.

    (b) Find the fraction which is equal to $0.\dot{2}$.
       Give your answer in its simplest terms.

2 Simplify.   (a) $2\sqrt{5} + 3\sqrt{5}$ (b) $\sqrt{3} \times \sqrt{3}$ (c) $\sqrt{2} \times \sqrt{3} \times \sqrt{6}$ (d) $\sqrt{\frac{9}{16}}$

3 (a) Write the number $0.4\dot{5}$ as a fraction in its simplest form.

    (b) Jim says, "When you multiply two irrational numbers together the answer is always an irrational number."
       Is Jim correct? Give a reason for your answer.

4 Write the recurring decimal $0.4\dot{8}$ in the form $\frac{a}{b}$, where a and b are integers.   Edexcel

5 (a) Express 12 as the product of its prime factors.

    (b) $\sqrt{12}$ can be written in the form of $a\sqrt{b}$ where a and b are prime numbers.
       Calculate the values of a and b.

6 Write $\sqrt{18}$ in the form of $a\sqrt{b}$ where a and b are prime numbers.

7 Simplify, leaving your answers where appropriate in surd form.

    (a) $5\sqrt{3} - \sqrt{3}$ (b) $\sqrt{3} \times 3\sqrt{3}$ (c) $\frac{\sqrt{27}}{3}$ (d) $\sqrt{12} \times \sqrt{75}$

8 Simplify fully.

    (a) $\sqrt{45}$ (b) $\sqrt{45} + \sqrt{20}$ (c) $\frac{\sqrt{45}}{\sqrt{20}}$ (d) $\left(\sqrt{45} - \sqrt{20}\right)^2$

9 Simplify the expression $\sqrt{24}\left(\sqrt{50} - \sqrt{8}\right)$.

10 Express each of the following in its simplest form with a rational denominator.

    (a) $\frac{6}{\sqrt{3}}$ (b) $\frac{15}{2\sqrt{5}}$

11 The area of this rectangle is $81\,\text{cm}^2$.
Work out the value of k.

$3^k\,$cm

$\sqrt{3}$ cm

Edexcel

12 (a) Find the value of

       (i) m when $\sqrt{128} = 2^m$,   (ii) n when $\left(\sqrt{8} - \sqrt{2}\right)^2 = 2^n$.

    A rectangle has a length of $2^t\,$cm and a width of $\left(\sqrt{8} - \sqrt{2}\right)$ cm.
    The area of the rectangle is $\sqrt{128}\,\text{cm}^2$.

    (b) Find t.   Edexcel

13 (a) n is a **rational** number. $k \times \sqrt{8} = n$
       Write down a non-zero value of k and a non-zero value of n which satisfy this equation.

    (b) Write $\sqrt{8}$ in the form 2^c, where c is a **rational** number.

    (c) $4^{d+1} = \sqrt{8}$.   Find the value of d.   Edexcel

14 You are given that $a = \sqrt{5} + 3$ and $b = \sqrt{5} - 3$.

    (a) $a + b = \sqrt{n}$.   Find the value of n.

    (b) Find the value of $\frac{a-b}{ab}$.

Section Review - Number ●●●●●●●●●●●●●

Do not use a calculator for questions 1 to 26.

1 Use these numbers to answer the following questions: | 2 | 12 | 27 | 36 | 80 | 88 |

    (a) Which number is a factor of 16?
    (b) Which number is a multiple of 16?
    (c) Which number is a prime number?
    (d) Which number is a square number?
    (e) Which number is a cube number?

2 (a) Work out   (i) $5 - 0.26$,   (ii) 0.2×0.4,   (iii) $24 \div 0.3$.
    (b) A turkey costs £2.40 per kilogram.
         What is the cost of a turkey which weighs 6.5 kilograms?

3 (a) Write these fractions in ascending order: $\frac{1}{2}$ $\frac{2}{3}$ $\frac{3}{5}$ $\frac{5}{8}$ $\frac{3}{4}$
    (b) Write down a fraction that lies halfway between $\frac{1}{5}$ and $\frac{1}{4}$.
    (c) Work out $\frac{2}{5}$ of 12.
    (d) Work out.   (i) $2\frac{2}{3} + 1\frac{4}{5}$ (ii) $2\frac{2}{3} - 1\frac{4}{5}$ (iii) $2\frac{2}{3} \times 1\frac{4}{5}$

4 Sarah uses the formula $t = \dfrac{2s}{u + v}$
     to work out the value of t when $s = 623.25$, $u = 11.37$ and $v = 87.22$.
     All the values are given to 2 decimal places.

     Sarah firstly estimates the value of t **without using her calculator**.
    (a) (i)   Write down the numbers Sarah could use in the formula to estimate the value of t.
         (ii)   Work out the estimate for the value of t that these numbers would give.

     Sarah then uses a calculator to work out the actual value of t.
    (b)   To what degree of accuracy would you give your calculator answer?
         Give a reason for your answer.
                                                               Edexcel

5 Two cucumbers and three lettuces cost £2.64.
     A cucumber costs 25% more than a lettuce. Find the cost of a lettuce.

6 Three cups of tea cost £2.85. How much will five cups of tea cost?

7 A plane flies a distance of 1800 miles at an average speed of 500 miles per hour.
     How long does the plane take for the journey?
     Give your answer in hours and minutes.

8 (a) Which is smaller 3^5 or 5^3?   Show all your working.
    (b) Work out.   (i) $2^5 \times 3^2$ (ii) $30^3 \div 6^2$

9 A crowd of 54 000 people watch a carnival.
     $\frac{2}{3}$ of the crowd are children and $\frac{3}{5}$ of the children are girls.
     What percentage of the crowd are girls?

10 Cas cycles 24 km at 15 km/h. She sets off at 0930. At what time does she finish?

11 The prime factors of a certain number are $2^3 \times 3 \times 11$.   What is the number?   Edexcel

12 Write these numbers in standard form.   (a)   38 600 000   (b)   0.000 054

13 (a) Given that $59 \times 347 = 20\ 473$,   find the exact value of $\frac{20\ 473}{590}$.
    (b) Use approximations to estimate the value of $\frac{97.3 \times 3049}{0.49}$.   Show all your working.
    (c) Work out $\sqrt{0.25} \times 0.1^2$.

20

14 Jack shares £180 between his two children Ruth and Ben.
The ratio of Ruth's share to Ben's share is 5 : 4.
(a) Work out how much each child is given.

Ben then gives 10% of his share to Ruth.
(b) Work out the percentage of the £180 that Ruth now has.   *Edexcel*

15 (a) Write 72 as a product of its prime factors.
(b) Write 96 as a product of its prime factors.
(c) Hence find (i) the least common multiple of 72 and 96,
               (ii) the highest common factor of 72 and 96.

16 Work out an estimate for the value of $\dfrac{29.91 - 2 \times 10.03}{29.91^2 - 10.03^2}$
Give your answer as a fraction in its simplest form.   *Edexcel*

17 (a) Write 4×10^5 as an ordinary number.
(b) Multiply 4×10^5 by 6×10^3. Give your answer in standard form.

18 Felix and Jan are in cars travelling in opposite directions along a motorway.
At 1015 they are 30 km apart and travelling towards each other.
Felix is travelling at an average speed of 70 km/h.
If they pass each other at 1027, what is Jan's average speed?

19 The ratio of male to female passengers on a bus is 3 : 5.
At the next stop 5 females get off and 2 males get on.
The ratio of male to female passengers is now 4 : 5.
How many male passengers are now on the bus?

20 The number 10^{100} is called a googol.
(a) Write the number 50 googols in standard index form.

A nanometre is 10^{-9} metres.
(b) Write 50 nanometres, in metres.
     Give your answer in standard index form.   *Edexcel*

21 In a sale all the prices are reduced by 30%.
The sale price of a jacket is £28.
Work out the price of the jacket before the sale.   *Edexcel*

22 (a) Write 240 as the product of its prime factors.
(b) Hence find the smallest whole number 240 must be multiplied by to give a perfect square.

23 It takes 15 minutes to fill a paddling pool at the rate of 12 litres per minute.
How long will it take to fill the pool at the rate of 20 litres per minute?

24 (a) Express $81^{-\frac{1}{2}}$ as a fraction in the form $\dfrac{a}{b}$ where a and b are integers.

(b) Find the value of y for which $2 \times 4^y = 64$.   *Edexcel*

25 (a) What is the reciprocal of 2.5?
(b) Write these numbers in descending order.

$$5^{-1} \qquad \left(\tfrac{1}{4}\right)^{\frac{1}{2}} \qquad 2^{-3} \qquad 3^{-2} \qquad \left(\tfrac{1}{2}\right)^2$$

(c) Find the value of x when:
     (i) $2^4 \times 2^3 = 2^x$,   (ii) $3^{-2} \div 3^{-4} = 3^x$,   (iii) $216^{\frac{1}{3}} = 6^x$.

(d) Work out $9^{-\frac{3}{2}}$. Give your answer as a fraction.

26 Evaluate $\dfrac{(23.4 + 35.6) \times 5.7}{200.3 \times (16.2 - 8.15)}$ *Edexcel*

27 In England, a jar of **extra fruity** apricot jam weighs 454 g and costs 89p.
In France, a jar of **extra fruity** apricot jam weighs 681 g and costs 1.84 euros.
  £1 = 1.58 euros.
In which country is the jam better value for money?
You must show all your working.

28 (a) Write the following fractions as decimals, writing all the figures shown on your calculator.
  (i) $\frac{9}{10}$ (ii) $\frac{45}{51}$

(b) Work out a fraction that is between $\frac{9}{10}$ and $\frac{45}{51}$ in size.   Edexcel

29 (a) What is the reciprocal of 0.35? Give your answer correct to two decimal places.

(b) Work out $\frac{3.2^2}{\sqrt{0.04}}$.

30 A caravan is for sale at £7200.
Stuart buys the caravan on credit.
The credit terms are:

> deposit 25% of sale price and 36 monthly payments of £175.

Express the extra amount paid for credit, compared with the cash price,
as a percentage of the cash price.

31 Karina says, "For some numbers the square root of the number is larger than the number itself."
For what numbers is this true?

32 At 20 miles per hour a bus journey takes 40 minutes.
A taxi does the same journey at 25 miles per hour.
How many minutes does the taxi take?

33 A shop buys Indian rugs from a factory.
In July, the cost to the shop of buying a rug was £100.
The shop bought 800 rugs in July.
In August, the cost to the shop of buying a rug increased by 10%.
The number of rugs bought by the shop decreased by 25%.
Find the difference between the total cost to the shop of all the rugs bought in July and the total
cost of all the rugs bought by the shop in August.   Edexcel

34 £1 can buy 1.54 euros. £1 can buy 1.37 dollars.
How many dollars can be bought with 1000 euros?

35 (a) Place the following numbers in descending order. $\sqrt{6.9}$ 2.58 1.6^2 $2\frac{4}{7}$

(b) (i) Calculate $\frac{612 \times 29.6}{81.3 - 18.9}$.
  Give your answer correct to 3 significant figures.
 (ii) Use approximations to show that your answer is about right.
  Show all your working.

36 In 2002, the population of the World was estimated to be 6340 million.
If the population increases at the rate of 1.7% per year, estimate the population of the World
in 2005.
Give your answer correct to 3 significant figures.

37 The selling price of a computer is
the **list price** plus VAT at $17\frac{1}{2}$%.

The selling price of a computer is £1292.50.
Work out the **list price** of this computer.

Selling price =
list price +
VAT

Edexcel

38 $p = 3^2 \times 5 \times 7$ and $q = 2 \times 3 \times 5^2$. Find the least common multiple of p and q.

39 The population of China is 1.2×10^9. The area of China is 9.5×10^6 square kilometres. What is the population density of China?

40 (a) You are given the formula $k = \frac{3}{4} m^2$.
Calculate the exact value of k, when $m = 4.8 \times 10^3$. Give your answer in standard form.

(b) Calculate $\sqrt{\dfrac{5.2 \times 10^{-3}}{(0.039)^2}}$ correct to two decimal places.

41 (a) Jools invests £2000 at 6.5% per annum compound interest.
Calculate the value of his investment at the end of 3 years.

(b) Jennifer gets 6% per annum on her investment.
After one year the value of her investment is £1272.
How much did she invest?

42 Last year Alf had a tax allowance of £4615 and paid £4328 in tax. The rates of tax were:

> 10p in the £ on the first £1920 of taxable income and
> 22p in the £ on all the remaining taxable income.

How much did Alf earn last year?

43 Calculate the value of $\dfrac{5.98 \times 10^8 + 4.32 \times 10^9}{6.14 \times 10^{-2}}$

Give your answer in standard form correct to 3 significant figures.   Edexcel

44 n is a positive integer such that $\sqrt{n} = 15.4$ correct to 1 decimal place.
(a) (i) Find a value of n.
(ii) Explain why $\sqrt{n}$ is irrational.
(b) Write down a number between 10 and 11 that has a rational square root.   Edexcel

45 A greengrocer buys apples and resells them at a profit of 12%.
How much did the greengrocer pay for apples which are sold for 84 pence?

46 Write the recurring decimal 0.353535… as a fraction in the form $\frac{x}{y}$, where x and y are integers.
                                                                                    Edexcel

47 The land are of France is 5.41×10^5 square kilometres.
The land area of the Earth is 1.32×10^8 square kilometres.
Calculate the land area of France as a percentage of the land area of the Earth.
Give your answer to a suitable degree of accuracy.

48 (a) Write $\sqrt{45}$ in the form $a\sqrt{b}$ where a and b are prime numbers.

(b) Write $\dfrac{5}{\sqrt{10}}$ in the form $\dfrac{\sqrt{a}}{b}$ where a and b are whole numbers.

(c) Express $\sqrt{32}$ as a power of 2.

(d) Simplify $4^0 + 4^{-1} + 4^{-2}$.

(e) Write $0.2\dot{7}$ as a fraction in its simplest form.

49 Calculate the value of $(5.8 \times 10^{-5})^{\frac{1}{3}}$.
Give your answer in standard form correct to 2 significant figures.

50 (a) Write $0.0\dot{4}$ as a fraction in its simplest form.
(b) Simplify (i) $\sqrt{12} + \sqrt{75}$ (ii) $\sqrt{12} \times \sqrt{75}$

(c) Rationalise $\dfrac{\sqrt{27} - \sqrt{12}}{\sqrt{15}}$

Section Review · · · · Section Review · · · ·

Introduction to Algebra ●●●

What you need to know

- You should be able to write **algebraic expressions**.

  Eg 1　An expression for the cost of 6 pens at n pence each is $6n$ pence.

  Eg 2　An expression for 2 pence more than n pence is $n + 2$ pence.

- Be able to **simplify expressions** by collecting **like terms** together.

  Eg 3　(a)　$2d + 3d = 5d$　　　(b)　$3x + 2 - x + 4 = 2x + 6$　(c)　$x + 2x + x^2 = 3x + x^2$

- Be able to **multiply expressions** together.

  Eg 4　(a)　$2a \times a = 2a^2$　　　(b)　$y \times y \times y = y^3$　　　(c)　$3m \times 2n = 6mn$

- Recall and use these properties of powers:
  Powers of the same base are **added** when terms are **multiplied**.
  Powers of the same base are **subtracted** when terms are **divided**.
  Powers are **multiplied** when a power is raised to a power.

  $$a^m \times a^n = a^{m+n}$$
  $$a^m \div a^n = a^{m-n}$$
  $$(a^m)^n = a^{m \times n}$$

  Eg 5　(a)　$x^3 \times x^2 = x^5$　(b)　$a^5 \div a^2 = a^3$　　(c)　$6m^6 \div 2m^2 = 3m^4$　(d)　$(2y^2)^3 = 8y^6$

- How to **multiply out brackets**.

  Eg 6　(a)　$2(x - 5) = 2x - 10$　　(b)　$x(x - 5) = x^2 - 5x$　　(c)　$2m(m + 3) = 2m^2 + 6m$

- How to **factorise expressions**.

  Eg 7　(a)　$3x - 6 = 3(x - 2)$　　(b)　$m^2 + 5m = m(m + 5)$　　(c)　$3a^2 - 6a = 3a(a - 2)$

Exercise 10

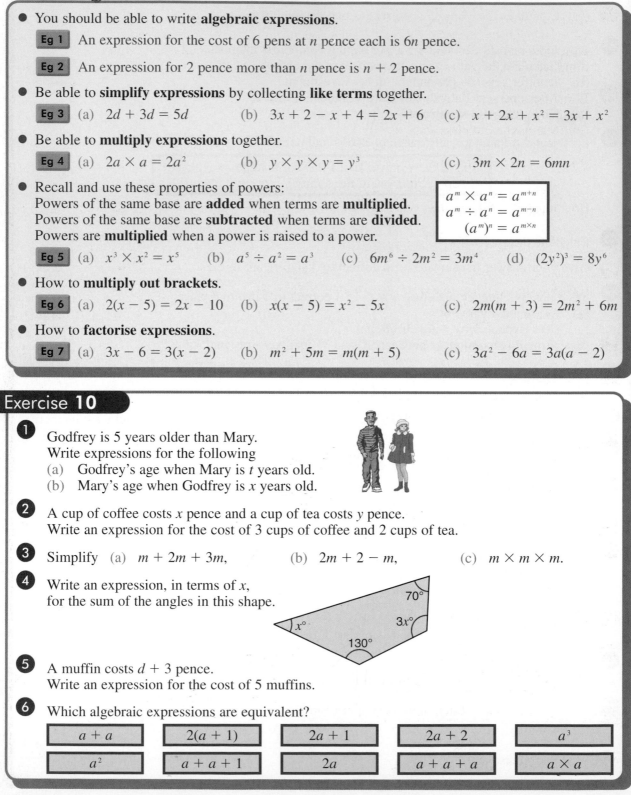

1　Godfrey is 5 years older than Mary.
Write expressions for the following
(a)　Godfrey's age when Mary is t years old.
(b)　Mary's age when Godfrey is x years old.

2　A cup of coffee costs x pence and a cup of tea costs y pence.
Write an expression for the cost of 3 cups of coffee and 2 cups of tea.

3　Simplify　(a)　$m + 2m + 3m$,　　　(b)　$2m + 2 - m$,　　　(c)　$m \times m \times m$.

4　Write an expression, in terms of x,
for the sum of the angles in this shape.

5　A muffin costs $d + 3$ pence.
Write an expression for the cost of 5 muffins.

6　Which algebraic expressions are equivalent?

$a + a$	$2(a + 1)$	$2a + 1$	$2a + 2$	a^3
a^2	$a + a + 1$	$2a$	$a + a + a$	$a \times a$

7 (a) Simplify (i) $2x + 3 + x$, (ii) $2x + y - x + y$.
(b) Multiply out (i) $2(x + 3)$, (ii) $x(x - 1)$.
(c) Multiply out and simplify (i) $2(x - 1) - 3$, (ii) $7 + 3(2 + x)$.
(d) Factorise (i) $2a - 6$, (ii) $x^2 + 2x$.

8 (a) Simplify $2ab + 3a - 2b + b - 5a + ab$.
(b) Multiply out and simplify $3(2x + 3) + 2(5 + x)$.

9 Ahmed and Hussein are two brothers. Ahmed is older than Hussein.
Given that Ahmed's age is $(5x - 4)$ years and Hussein's age is $(2x + 1)$ years,
write down an expression, in terms of x, for how much older Ahmed is than Hussein.
Simplify your answer. *Edexcel*

10 Lorna buys some 1st class stamps and some 2nd class stamps.
She buys 12 stamps altogether.
(a) She buys x 1st class stamps.
Write an expression for the number of 2nd class stamps she buys.
(b) 2nd class stamps cost d pence.
A 1st class stamp costs 5 pence more than a 2nd class stamp.
Write an expression for the cost of a 1st class stamp.
(c) Write an expression, in terms of x and d, for the amount Lorna has to pay for her 12 stamps.

11 Simplify. (a) $y^3 \times y^2$ (b) $x^6 \div x^3$ (c) $\dfrac{z^4 \times z}{z^3}$ (d) $\dfrac{x^2 y}{xy^2}$

12 (a) Multiply out $t^2(t^3 - t^4)$.
(b) Multiply out and simplify $3(2a + 6) - 2(3a - 6)$.
(c) Simplify $\dfrac{12a^2 b}{4ab}$. *Edexcel*

13 Factorise completely (a) $x^2 - 3x$, (b) $2p^2 q + pq^2$. *Edexcel*

14 (a) Simplify $5 - 3(2n - 1)$.
(b) Multiply out $(-3m) \times (-2m)$.
(c) Factorise fully $8mn - 2m$.

15 (a) Simplify (i) $2a^3 \times 3a$, (ii) $6x^8 \div 3x^2$, (iii) $\dfrac{3m^2 \times 4n^6}{6mn^2}$, (iv) $4x^3 y \times 5x^2 y$.
(b) Expand (i) $(3m^3)^2$, (ii) $(2a^2 b)^3$.

16 (a) $x^2 \times x^3 = x^p$. Write down the value of p.
(b) $\sqrt{x} = x^q$. Write down the value of q.
(c) $(x^2 \times x^3) \div \sqrt{x} = x^r$. Find the value of r. *Edexcel*

17 (a) Expand the brackets. (i) $2x(x - 3y)$ (ii) $3a(3a + a^2)$
(b) Factorise. (i) $4xy - 2y^2$ (ii) $3m^2 - 12m$
(c) Simplify. $2x^2 - x(1 + x)$

18 Simplify fully. $\dfrac{4a^2 b^3 \times 3a^3 b}{6a^5 b^2}$

19 (a) Multiply out $2x(2y - xy)$.
(b) Factorise $6pq - 3pq^2$.
(c) Simplify $21m^6 \div 7m^3$.

20 Simplify. (a) $\dfrac{6x^2 z \times 2x^2 y^2 z}{3x^3 y}$ (b) $\sqrt{\dfrac{1}{m^6}}$ (c) $(4x^2 y)^3$

21 Simplify fully $\dfrac{3a^2}{bc} \times \dfrac{b^2}{6ac^2} \times \dfrac{2ac^2}{b}$.

Introduction to Algebra

SECTION 11 Solving Equations

What you need to know

- The solution of an equation is the value of the unknown letter that fits the equation.
- You should be able to solve simple equations by **inspection**.
- Be able to solve simple problems by **working backwards**.

Eg 1 I think of a number, multiply it by 3 and add 4. The answer is 19.

x → multiply by 3 → add 4 → Answer 19

5 ← divide by 3 ← 15 ← subtract 4 ← 19

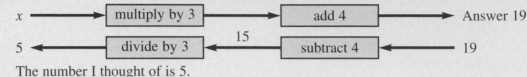

The number I thought of is 5.

- Be able to use the **balance method** to solve equations.

Eg 2 Solve these equations.

(a) $d - 13 = -5$
$d = -5 + 13$
$d = 8$

(b) $-4a = 20$
$a = \frac{20}{-4}$
$a = -5$

(c) $5 - 4n = -1$
$-4n = -6$
$n = 1.5$

- Be able to solve equations with unknowns on both sides of the equals sign.

Eg 3 Solve $3x + 1 = x + 7$.

$3x = x + 6$
$2x = 6$
$x = 3$

- Be able to solve equations which include brackets.

Eg 4 Solve $4(3 + 2x) = 5(x + 2)$.

$12 + 8x = 5x + 10$
$8x = 5x - 2$
$3x = -2$
$x = -\frac{2}{3}$

- Be able to solve equations which involve fractions.

Eg 5 Solve $\frac{x}{2} + \frac{2x}{3} = 7$.

$6 \times \frac{x}{2} + 6 \times \frac{2x}{3} = 6 \times 7$
$3x + 4x = 42$
$7x = 42$
$x = 6$

Eg 6 Solve $\frac{x-1}{3} = \frac{x+1}{4}$.

$4(x - 1) = 3(x + 1)$
$4x - 4 = 3x + 3$
$4x = 3x + 7$
$x = 7$

- You should be able to write, or form, equations using the information given in a problem.

Exercise 11

1 Solve these equations. (a) $7 + x = 12$ (b) $5 - x = 3$ (c) $5x - 9 = 11$

2 (a) I think of a number, add 3, and then multiply by 2.
The answer is 16. What is my number?
(b) I think of a number, double it and then subtract 3.
The answer is 5. What is my number?

3 Solve these equations.
(a) $3x - 7 = 23$ (b) $5 + 7x = 47$ (c) $5(x - 2) = 20$ (d) $3x - 7 = x + 15$

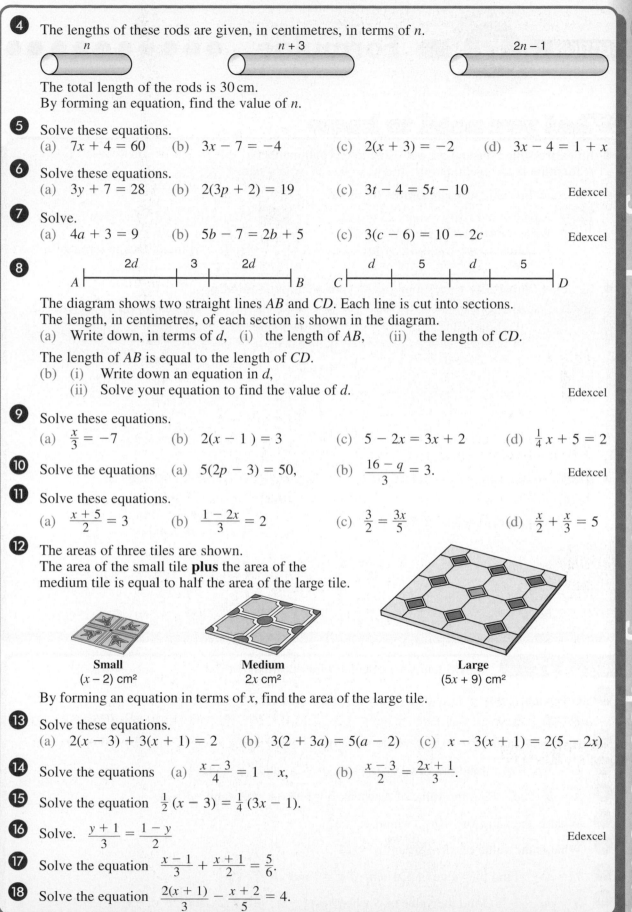

4 The lengths of these rods are given, in centimetres, in terms of n.

n $n + 3$ $2n - 1$

The total length of the rods is $30\,cm$.
By forming an equation, find the value of n.

5 Solve these equations.
(a) $7x + 4 = 60$ (b) $3x - 7 = -4$ (c) $2(x + 3) = -2$ (d) $3x - 4 = 1 + x$

6 Solve these equations.
(a) $3y + 7 = 28$ (b) $2(3p + 2) = 19$ (c) $3t - 4 = 5t - 10$ Edexcel

7 Solve.
(a) $4a + 3 = 9$ (b) $5b - 7 = 2b + 5$ (c) $3(c - 6) = 10 - 2c$ Edexcel

8

A |———$2d$———|——3——|———$2d$———| B C |———d———|——5——|———d———|——5——| D

The diagram shows two straight lines AB and CD. Each line is cut into sections.
The length, in centimetres, of each section is shown in the diagram.
(a) Write down, in terms of d,   (i) the length of AB,   (ii) the length of CD.

The length of AB is equal to the length of CD.
(b) (i) Write down an equation in d,
     (ii) Solve your equation to find the value of d.   Edexcel

9 Solve these equations.
(a) $\frac{x}{3} = -7$ (b) $2(x - 1) = 3$ (c) $5 - 2x = 3x + 2$ (d) $\frac{1}{4}x + 5 = 2$

10 Solve the equations   (a) $5(2p - 3) = 50,$ (b) $\frac{16 - q}{3} = 3.$ Edexcel

11 Solve these equations.
(a) $\frac{x + 5}{2} = 3$ (b) $\frac{1 - 2x}{3} = 2$ (c) $\frac{3}{2} = \frac{3x}{5}$ (d) $\frac{x}{2} + \frac{x}{3} = 5$

12 The areas of three tiles are shown.
The area of the small tile **plus** the area of the
medium tile is equal to half the area of the large tile.

Small   **Medium**   **Large**
$(x - 2)\ cm^2$ $2x\ cm^2$ $(5x + 9)\ cm^2$

By forming an equation in terms of x, find the area of the large tile.

13 Solve these equations.
(a) $2(x - 3) + 3(x + 1) = 2$ (b) $3(2 + 3a) = 5(a - 2)$ (c) $x - 3(x + 1) = 2(5 - 2x)$

14 Solve the equations   (a) $\frac{x - 3}{4} = 1 - x,$ (b) $\frac{x - 3}{2} = \frac{2x + 1}{3}.$

15 Solve the equation $\frac{1}{2}(x - 3) = \frac{1}{4}(3x - 1).$

16 Solve. $\frac{y + 1}{3} = \frac{1 - y}{2}$ Edexcel

17 Solve the equation $\frac{x - 1}{3} + \frac{x + 1}{2} = \frac{5}{6}.$

18 Solve the equation $\frac{2(x + 1)}{3} - \frac{x + 2}{5} = 4.$

What you need to know

- An **expression** is just an answer using letters and numbers.
  A **formula** is an algebraic rule. It always has an equals sign.

- You should be able to **write simple formulae**.

  Eg 1 A packet of crisps weighs 25 grams.
  Write a formula for the total weight,
  W grams, of n packets of crisps.
  $$W = 25n$$

  Eg 2 Start with t, add 5 and then multiply
  by 3. The result is p.
  Write a formula for p in terms of t.
  $$p = 3(t + 5)$$

- Be able to **substitute** values into given expressions and formulae.

  Eg 3
  (a) $A = pq - r$
  Find the value
  of A when $p = 2$,
  $q = -2$ and $r = 3$.
  $$A = pq - r$$
  $$= 2 \times (-2) - 3$$
  $$= -4 - 3$$
  $$= -7$$

  (b) $M = 2n^2$
  Find the value
  of M when $n = 3$.
  $$M = 2n^2$$
  $$= 2 \times 3^2$$
  $$= 2 \times 9$$
  $$= 18$$

  (c) Find the value of $\dfrac{b^2 c}{d}$
  when $b = \frac{1}{2}$, $c = 4.8$
  and $d = -3$.
  $$\frac{b^2 c}{d} = \frac{\left(\frac{1}{2}\right)^2 \times 4.8}{-3}$$
  $$= \frac{\frac{1}{4} \times 4.8}{-3} = \frac{1.2}{-3}$$
  $$= -0.4$$

- Be able to **rearrange** a given formula to make another letter (variable) the subject.

  Eg 4 $y = 2x + a$

  Make x the subject of the formula.

  $$y = 2x + a$$
  $$y - a = 2x$$
  $$\frac{y - a}{2} = x$$
  So, $x = \dfrac{y - a}{2}$

  Eg 5 $T = ab^2$
  Rearrange the formula to give b
  in terms of T and a.

  $$T = ab^2$$
  $$\frac{T}{a} = b^2$$
  $$b = \pm \sqrt{\frac{T}{a}}$$

Exercise 12

Do not use a calculator for questions 1 to 11.

1 Given that $m = -3$ and $n = 5$, find the value of
(a) $m + n$,   (b) $m - n$,   (c) $n - m$,   (d) mn.

2 If $p = 4$ and $q = -5$ find the value of   (a) $3pq$,   (b) $p^2 + 2q$.

3 $L = 5(p + q)$. Find the value of L when $p = 2$ and $q = -0.4$.

4 $A = b - cd$. Find the value of A when $b = -3$, $c = 2$ and $d = 4$.

5 What is the value of $10y^2$ when $y = 3$?

6 What is the value of $3x^3$ when $x = 2$?

7 $T = ab^2$. Find the value of T when $a = 4$ and $b = -5$.

8 $S = pq - 2r^2$. Find the value of S when $p = -5$, $q = -2$ and $r = -3$.

9 $T = \frac{uv}{w}$. Find the value of T when $u = 3$, $v = -2$ and $w = \frac{1}{2}$.

10 $M = \sqrt{\frac{a}{b}}$. Find the value of M when $a = 8$ and $b = \frac{1}{2}$.

11 A pen costs 25 pence.
A pencil costs 10 pence.
Louisa buys x pens and y pencils.
The total cost is C pence.
(a) Write a formula for C in terms of x and y.
(b) Work out the value of y when $C = 250$ and $x = 6$.

Edexcel

12 $c = y - mx$. Calculate the value of c when $y = 4.95$, $m = -0.75$ and $x = 3$. Edexcel

13 A formula is given as $c = 3t - 5$. Rearrange the formula to give t in terms of c.

14 $s = \frac{1}{2}(u + v)t$. Work out the value of s when $u = 10$, $v = -25$ and $t = 0.5$. Edexcel

15 Rearrange the formula $n = 3 + mp$ to make m the subject.

16 The diagram shows a solid.
The volume, V, of the solid is given by the formula

$$V = \frac{\pi h}{3}(R^2 + Rr + r^2)$$

(a) $h = 6.8$, $R = 9.7$ and $r = 5.3$
Calculate the value of V.
Give your answer correct to 3 significant figures.
(b) Make h the subject of the formula.
(c) $V = 200$, $h = 10$ and $R = 2r$. Calculate the value of R.
Give your answer correct to 3 significant figures.

Edexcel

17 $m = \frac{3}{5}(n - 17)$. Find the value of n when $m = -9$.

18 Make r the subject of the formula $p = \frac{gr}{s}$.

19 You are given the formula $v = u + at$.
(a) Find v when $u = 17$, $a = -8$ and $t = \frac{3}{5}$.
(b) Rearrange the formula to give a in terms of v, u and t.

20 Make s the subject of the formula $t = s^2 + 5$.

21 Make x the subject of the formula $y = \frac{x^2 + 4}{5}$. Edexcel

22 $v^2 = u^2 + 2as$. Calculate the value of v, when $u = 8$, $a = -3$ and $s = 5.5$. Edexcel

23 You are given the formula $g = \frac{3}{5}h^2$.
(a) Find the value of g when $h = 2.5 \times 10^3$.
(b) Rearrange the formula to give h in terms of g.

24 Rearrange the formula $p = \frac{q}{5 - q}$ to make q the subject.

25 Make v the subject of the formula $w = \frac{uv}{u + v}$.

26 $n = \frac{3 + m}{m - 5}$. Rearrange the formula to give m in terms of n.

27 Rearrange $4y = k(2 - 3y)$ to write y in terms of k. Edexcel

Formulae .... Formulae .... Formulae ....

Direct and Inverse Proportion

What you need to know

- **Direct proportion**

  If x and y are quantities such that $y : x^n$ is always constant, then y varies **directly** with x^n.

  This can be expressed:
  - in **words**: y is **proportional** to x^n,
  - in **symbols**: $y \propto x^n$ (where $\propto$ means "is proportional to"),
  - as an **equation**: $y = kx^n$ (where k is the **constant of proportionality**).

  Eg 1 The cost, $£C$, of tiling a floor is proportional to the area of the floor, $a\,m^2$.
  It costs £60 to tile a floor of area $2\,m^2$.
  (a) Find the formula connecting C and a.
  (b) A floor costs £150 to be tiled. What is the area of the floor?

  (a) $C = ka$
  When $C = 60$, $a = 2$.
  $60 = 2 \times k$
  $k = 30$
  $C = 30a$

  (b) $C = 30a$
  When $C = 150$.
  $150 = 30a$
  $a = 5$
  Area of floor = $5\,m^2$

  > Constant of proportionality, k.
  > This can be calculated when corresponding values of C and a are known.

- **Inverse proportion**

  If x and y are quantities such that $y : \dfrac{1}{x^n}$ is always constant, then y varies **inversely** with x^n.

  This can be expressed:
  - in **words**: y is **inversely proportional** to x^n,
  - in **symbols**: $y \propto \dfrac{1}{x^n}$,
  - as an **equation**: $y = \dfrac{k}{x^n}$ or $x^n y = k$.

  Eg 2 y is inversely proportional to x^2. When $x = 3$, $y = 4$.
  (a) Find the equation connecting y and x. (b) Find the value of y when $x = 2.4$.

  (a) $y = \dfrac{k}{x^2}$

  When $x = 3$, $y = 4$.

  $4 = \dfrac{k}{3^2}$ so $k = 36$

  $y = \dfrac{36}{x^2}$

  (b) $y = \dfrac{36}{x^2}$

  When $x = 2.4$.

  $y = \dfrac{36}{(2.4)^2}$

  $y = 6.25$

- The general form of a proportional relationship is $y \propto x^n$ or $y = kx^n$.

  Direct proportion, $y = kx^n$, $n > 0$

  When:
  $n = 1$: y increases at a constant rate.
  $0 < n < 1$: y increases at a rate that decreases.
  $n > 1$: y increases at a rate that increases.

  Inverse proportion, $y = kx^n$, $n < 0$

  When:
  $n = -1$: the graph is symmetrical about the line $y = x$.

1 The table shows values of m and n.
  (a) Show that m is directly proportional to n.
  (b) Find the value of (i) m when $n = 1.8$,
     (ii) n when $m = 12.6$.

m	0.6	9	16.5
n	0.4	6	11

2 The distance (d metres) travelled by a stone falling vertically varies in direct proportion to the square of the time (t seconds) for which it falls.
  (a) Write a formula to connect d, t and the constant of variation k.

  A stone takes 2 seconds to fall 20 metres.
  (b) Find the value of k.
  (c) How far will the stone fall in 4 seconds?

  A stone is dropped from a balloon which is 500 metres above the ground.
  (d) How many seconds will the stone take to reach the ground?   *Edexcel*

3 y is proportional to x^3.
  When $x = 3$, $y = 54$.
  Find the value of x when $y = 250$.

4 F varies inversely as the square of d.
  $F = 50$ when $d = 10$.
  (a) Express F in terms of d.
  (b) (i) Calculate the value of F when $d = 1000$.
     (ii) Calculate the value of d when $F = 500$.   *Edexcel*

5 m is proportional to the square root of n.
     $m = 6$ when $n = 81$.
  (a) Find the equation connecting m and n.
  (b) Calculate (i) the value of m when $n = 36$,
            (ii) the value of n when $m = 10$.

6 An artist hand-paints circular plates of different sizes.
  The price, £C, of a hand-painted plate is proportional to the square of the radius, r cm, of the plate.
  The price of a plate of radius 6 cm is £9.
  Calculate the price of a plate of radius 8 cm.

7 y is directly proportional to the cube of x.
  When $x = 2$, $y = 64$.
  (a) Find an expression for y in terms of x.
  (b) Hence, or otherwise,
     (i) calculate the value of y when $x = \frac{1}{2}$,
     (ii) calculate the value of x when $y = 27$.   *Edexcel*

8 y is proportional to x^n.
  Sketch a graph of y against x when $x \geqslant 0$ and (a) $n = 2$,   (b) $n = -2$.

9 You are given that $y = 6x^n$ and that $y = 3$ when $x = 8$.
  Find the value of n.

10 y is directly proportional to x^2.
  When $x = 2$, $y = 36$.
  (a) Express y in terms of x.

  z is inversely proportional to x.
  When $x = 3$, $z = 2$.
  (b) Show that $z = cy^n$, where c and n are numbers and $c > 0$.
     (You must find the values of c and n).   *Edexcel*

Sequences ● ● ● ● ● ● ● ● ● ● ● ● ●

What you need to know

- A **sequence** is a list of numbers made according to some rule.
  The numbers in a sequence are called **terms**.

- You should be able to draw and continue number sequences represented by patterns of shapes.

- Be able to continue a sequence by following a given rule.

  Eg 1 The sequence 2, 7, 22, … is made using the rule:

  > multiply the last number by 3, then add 1.

  The next term in the sequence $= (22 \times 3) + 1 = 66 + 1 = 67$

- Be able to find a rule, and then use it, to continue a sequence.

  > **To continue a sequence:**
  > 1. Work out the rule to get from one term to the next.
  > 2. Apply the same rule to find further terms in the sequence.

  Eg 2 Describe the rule used to make the following sequences.
  Then use the rule to find the next term of each sequence.

(a) 5, 8, 11, 14, …	(b) 2, 4, 8, 16, …	(c) 1, 1, 2, 3, 5, 8, …
Rule:	Rule:	Rule:
add 3 to last term	multiply last term by 2	add the last two terms
Next term: 17	Next term: 32	Next term: 13

  > **Special sequences** **Square numbers:**   1, 4, 9, 16, 25, …
  > **Triangular numbers:** 1, 3, 6, 10, 15, …

- Find an expression for the n th term of a **linear sequence**.

  > A number sequence which increases (or decreases) by the same amount
  > from one term to the next is called a **linear sequence**.
  > The sequence 2, 8, 14, 20, 26, … has a **common difference** of 6.

  Eg 3 Find the n th term of the sequence: 3, 5, 7, 9, …
  The sequence is linear, common difference $= 2$.
  To find the n th term add one to the multiples of 2.
  So, the n th term is $2n + 1$.

- Find an expression for the n th term of a **quadratic sequence**.

  Eg 4 Find the n th term of the sequence: 4, 7, 12, 19, …
  The sequence is not linear, because the difference between terms is increasing.
  Compare the sequence with the sequence of square numbers: 1, 4, 9, 16, …
  To find the n th term add 3 to the square numbers.
  So, the n th term is $n^2 + 3$.

Exercise 14

1 What is the next number in each of these sequences?
    (a) 1, 2, 5, 10, ….
    (b) 1, 3, 9, 27, ….
    (c) 1, $\frac{1}{2}$, $\frac{1}{4}$, $\frac{1}{8}$, ….

2 Look at this sequence of numbers. 2, 5, 8, 11, ...
  (a) What is the next number in the sequence?
  (b) Is 30 a number in this sequence? Give a reason for your answer.

3 The rule for a sequence is:

> Add the last two numbers and divide by 2.

Write down the next three terms when the sequence begins: 3, 7, ...

4 A sequence begins: 1, 6, 10, 8, ...
  The rule to continue the sequence is:

  double the difference between the last two numbers.

  Ravi says if you continue the sequence it will end in 0. Is he correct? Explain your answer.

5 The first three patterns in a sequence are shown.

| Pattern 1 | Pattern 2 | Pattern 3 |

  (a) How many squares are in pattern 20?
      Explain how you found your answer.
  (b) Write an expression for the number of squares in the nth pattern.

6 Here are the first four terms of a number sequence: 3, 7, 11, 15.
  (a) Write down the next two terms of the sequence.
  (b) Write down an expression, in terms of n, for the nth term of the sequence. Edexcel

7 Find the nth term of the following sequences.
  (a) 5, 7, 9, 11, ...   (b) 1, 5, 9, 13, ...   (c) −2, −1, 0, 1, ...

8 Marco writes down a number sequence.
  He starts at 120.
  Each time he subtracts 12 to get the next number in the sequence.
  (a) Write down the first 5 numbers in the sequence.
  (b) Write down an expression for the nth number in the sequence. Edexcel

9 (a) Write down the first **three** terms of the sequence whose nth term is given by $n^2 - 4$.
  (b) Will the number 60 be in this sequence? Explain your answer.

10 A sequence begins: 3, 6, 11, 18, 27, ...
  (a) Find the next two terms in this sequence.
  (b) Explain why this is not a linear sequence.
  (c) Explain how you can find the 20th term in the sequence without writing down all the previous terms.

11 Find, in terms of n, the nth term of the sequence: $\frac{1}{3}$, $\frac{2}{5}$, $\frac{3}{7}$, $\frac{4}{9}$, $\frac{5}{11}$, ...

12 Give the nth term of the following sequences.
  (a) 1, 4, 9, 16, 25, 36, ...
  (b) 4, 7, 12, 19, 28, 39, ...
  (c) −1, 2, 7, 14, 23, 34, ...

13 Find the nth term of the sequence: 2, 8, 18, 32, 50, ...

14 The numbers 2, 6, 12, 20, ... form a number sequence.
  (a) Write down an expression, in terms of n, for the nth term in the sequence.
  (b) Work out the difference between the nth term and the $(n + 1)$th term.
      Give your answer as simply as you can, in terms of n. Edexcel

Straight Line Graphs ● ● ● ● ●

What you need to know

- **Coordinates** (involving positive and negative numbers) are used to describe the position of a point on a graph.

- The x axis is the line $y = 0$.   The y axis is the line $x = 0$.

- The **gradient** of a line can be found by drawing a right-angled triangle.

$$\text{Gradient} = \frac{\text{distance up}}{\text{distance along}}$$

distance up

distance along

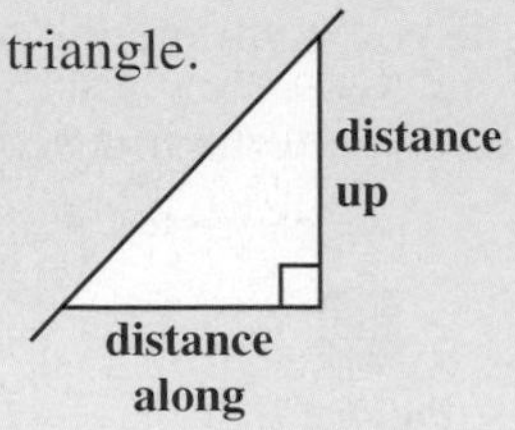

Gradients can be positive, zero or negative.

- You should be able to find the equation for a given line.

In general, the equation of any straight line can be written in the form

$$y = mx + c$$

where m is the **gradient** of the line
and c is the **y-intercept**.

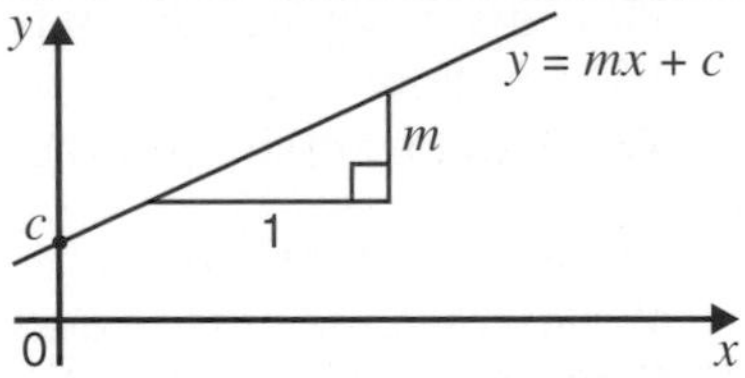

$y = mx + c$

Eg 1   Find the equation of the line shown on this graph.

Gradient of line $= \dfrac{\text{distance up}}{\text{distance along}} = \dfrac{2}{1} = 2$

The graph crosses the y axis at the point $(0, -3)$,
so the y-intercept is -3.
The equation of the line is $y = 2x - 3$.

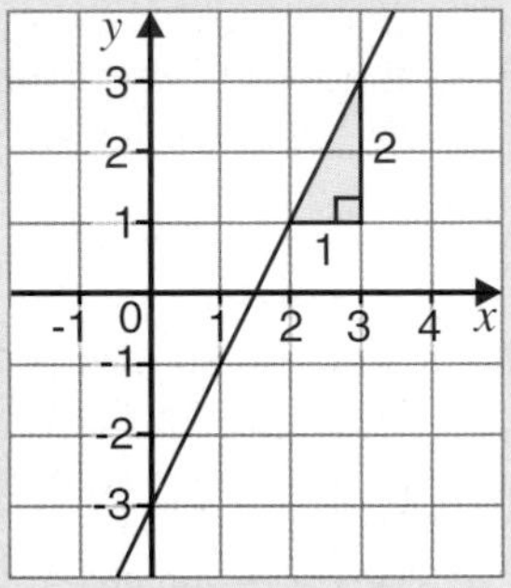

- The points where a line crosses the axes can be found:
  by reading the coordinates from a graph,
  by substituting $x = 0$ and $y = 0$ into the equation of the line.

Eg 2   The diagram shows a sketch of the line $2y = x + 3$.
Find the coordinates of the points P and Q.

When $x = 0$, $2y = 0 + 3$, $2y = 3$, $y = 1\frac{1}{2}$.
When $y = 0$, $0 = x + 3$, $x = -3$.
The points are $P\left(0, 1\frac{1}{2}\right)$ and $Q(-3, 0)$.

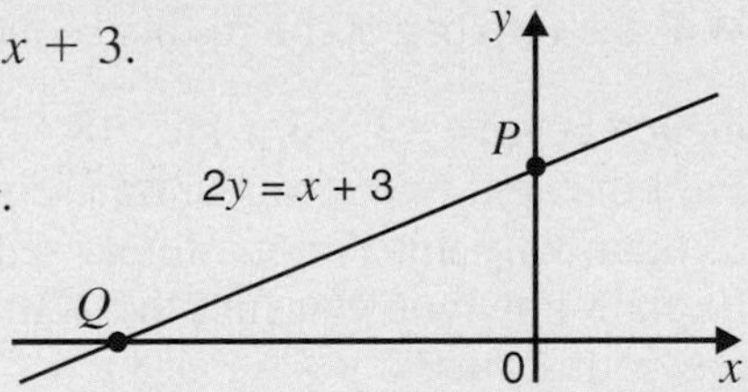

$2y = x + 3$

- You should be able to find the gradient of a line which is perpendicular to a given line.

If two lines are perpendicular to each other, the product of their gradients $= -1$.

This can be written as: $m_{AB} \times m_{CD} = -1$

where m_{AB} is the gradient of the line AB,
and m_{CD} is the gradient of the line CD.

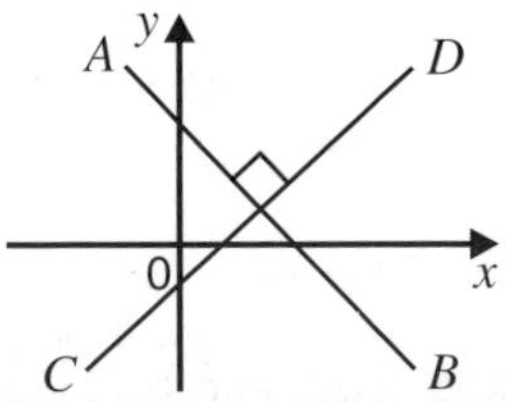

$$m_{AB} = \frac{-1}{m_{CD}}$$

Eg 3   Write down the gradient of the line which is perpendicular to the line with equation $y = -3x + 4$.
The gradient of the line $y = -3x + 4$ is -3.
The gradient of the line which is perpendicular to this line is $-1 \div (-3) = \frac{1}{3}$.

- Equations of the form $px + qy = r$ can be **rearranged** to the form $y = mx + c$.

Eg 4 The graph of a straight line is given by the equation $4y - 3x = 8$.
Write this equation in the form $y = mx + c$.
$$4y - 3x = 8$$
$$4y = 3x + 8$$
$$y = \frac{3}{4}x + 2$$

> The line has gradient $\frac{3}{4}$ and y-intercept 2.

- You should be able to solve equations and problems involving straight line graphs.

Exercise 15

1 (a) Copy and complete this table of values for $y = 2x + 3$.

x	-3	-2	-1	0	1	2
y		-1				

(b) Draw the graph of $y = 2x + 3$ for values of x from -3 to 2.
(c) Use your graph to find (i) the value of y when $x = 1.5$,
                                          (ii) the value of x when $y = -0.5$.

Edexcel

2 (a) On the same axes, draw the graphs of $y = -2$, $y = x$ and $x + y = 5$.
(b) Which of these lines has a negative gradient?

3 The diagram shows a sketch of the line $2y = 6 - x$.
(a) Find the coordinates of the points P and Q.
(b) The line $2y = 6 - x$ goes through $R(-5, m)$.
What is the value of m?

4 Points P, Q and R are shown on the grid.
(a) Write down the equation of the line PQ.
(b) (i) Use the grid to work out the gradient of the line RP.
(ii) Write down the equation of the line RP.

5 Match these equations to their graphs.

1 $y = 2x$
2 $y - x = 2$
3 $y + x = 2$
4 $2y = x$

P   Q   R   S

6 (a) Copy and complete the table of values for $2y = 3x - 6$.

x	-2	0	4
y		-3	

(b) Draw the graph of $2y = 3x - 6$ for values of x from -2 to 4.
(c) What is the gradient of the line $2y = 3x - 6$?
(d) Use your graph to find the value of x when $y = 1.5$.

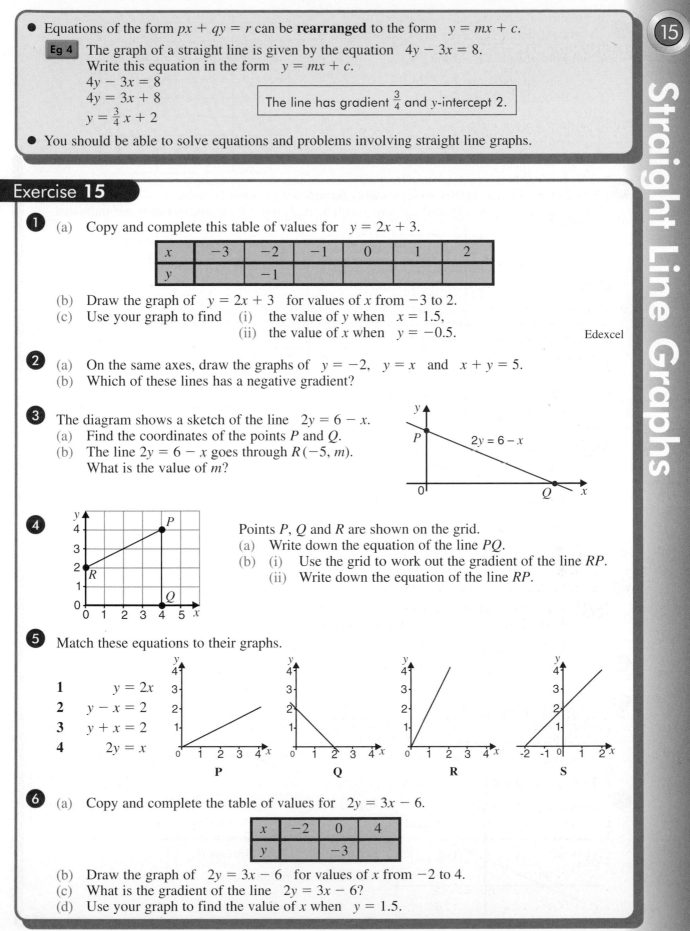

7 A straight line, L, has been drawn on the grid.

(a) Find an equation of the line L.

(b) Find an equation of the line through $(1, 2)$ parallel to L.

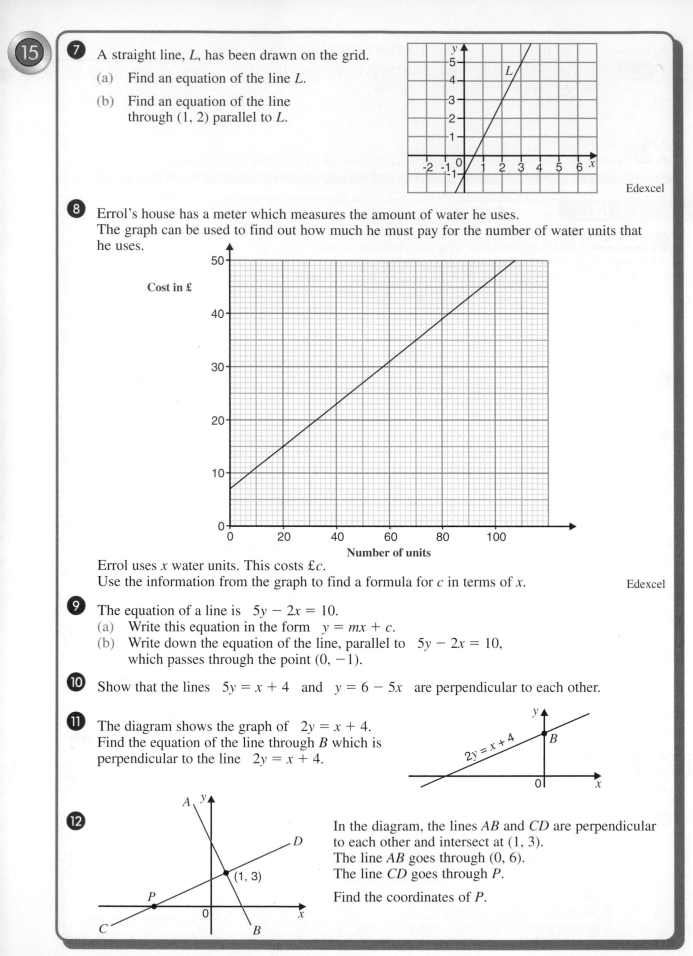

Edexcel

8 Errol's house has a meter which measures the amount of water he uses.
The graph can be used to find out how much he must pay for the number of water units that he uses.

Cost in £

Number of units

Errol uses x water units. This costs £c.
Use the information from the graph to find a formula for c in terms of x.

Edexcel

9 The equation of a line is $5y - 2x = 10$.
(a) Write this equation in the form $y = mx + c$.
(b) Write down the equation of the line, parallel to $5y - 2x = 10$, which passes through the point $(0, -1)$.

10 Show that the lines $5y = x + 4$ and $y = 6 - 5x$ are perpendicular to each other.

11 The diagram shows the graph of $2y = x + 4$.
Find the equation of the line through B which is perpendicular to the line $2y = x + 4$.

$2y = x + 4$

B

12

A

D

$(1, 3)$

P

C

B

In the diagram, the lines AB and CD are perpendicular to each other and intersect at $(1, 3)$.
The line AB goes through $(0, 6)$.
The line CD goes through P.

Find the coordinates of P.

Using Graphs ●●●●●●●●

What you need to know

- A **gradient** measures the **rate of change** of one quantity with respect to another.
  A **positive** gradient represents a **rate of increase**.
  A **negative** gradient represents a **rate of decrease**.

- The gradient of a **distance-time graph** gives the speed.

  > **Speed** is the rate of change of distance with respect to time.
  > When the distance-time graph is **linear** the **speed is constant**.
  > When the distance-time graph is **horizontal** the **speed is zero**.

Eg 1 The graph shows a car journey.
  (a) Between what times does the car travel fastest? Explain your answer.
  (b) What is the speed of the car during this part of the journey?

  (a) 1200 to 1230. Steepest gradient.

  (b) $\text{Speed} = \dfrac{\text{Distance}}{\text{Time}} = \dfrac{20\,\text{km}}{\frac{1}{2}\,\text{hour}} = 40\,\text{km/h}$

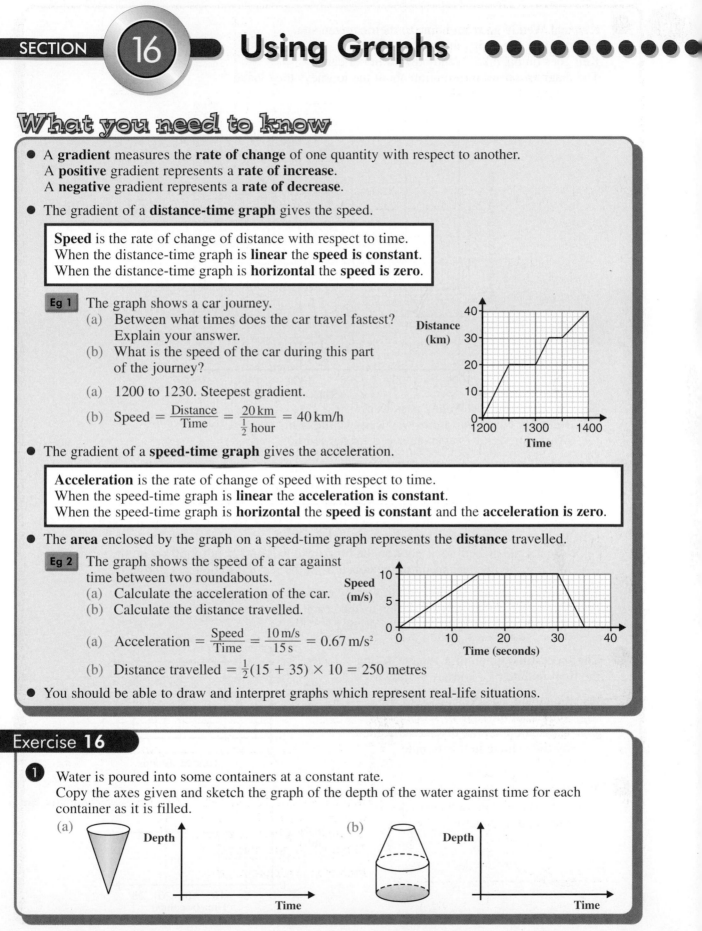

- The gradient of a **speed-time graph** gives the acceleration.

  > **Acceleration** is the rate of change of speed with respect to time.
  > When the speed-time graph is **linear** the **acceleration is constant**.
  > When the speed-time graph is **horizontal** the **speed is constant** and the **acceleration is zero**.

- The **area** enclosed by the graph on a speed-time graph represents the **distance** travelled.

Eg 2 The graph shows the speed of a car against time between two roundabouts.
  (a) Calculate the acceleration of the car.
  (b) Calculate the distance travelled.

  (a) $\text{Acceleration} = \dfrac{\text{Speed}}{\text{Time}} = \dfrac{10\,\text{m/s}}{15\,\text{s}} = 0.67\,\text{m/s}^2$

  (b) Distance travelled $= \frac{1}{2}(15 + 35) \times 10 = 250$ metres

- You should be able to draw and interpret graphs which represent real-life situations.

Exercise 16

1. Water is poured into some containers at a constant rate.
   Copy the axes given and sketch the graph of the depth of the water against time for each container as it is filled.

   (a)

   (b)

2 Ken and Wendy go from home to their caravan site.
The caravan site is 50 km from their home.
Ken goes on his bike. Wendy drives in her car.
The diagram shows information about the journeys they made.

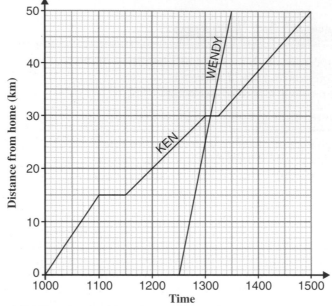

(a)   At what time did Wendy pass Ken?
(b)   Between which two times was Ken cycling at his greatest speed?
(c)   Work out Wendy's average speed for her journey.

Edexcel

3 A coach leaves Gateshead at 0830 to travel to London.
It completes the first 270 km of the journey at 90 km/hour before stopping at a service station.
The coach stops at the service station for 30 minutes.
After leaving the service station the coach travels a further 180 km, arriving in London at 1500.
(a)   Draw a distance-time graph for the coach journey.
       Use a scale of 2 cm for 1 hour on the horizontal axis and 1 cm for 50 km on the vertical axis.
(b)   What is the average speed of the coach from the service station to London?

Travis leaves London at 1000 and travels by car to Gateshead on the same route.
(c)   Travis gets to the service station as the coach is about to leave.
       At what average speed is Travis driving?

4 The speed-time graph of a vehicle during
the final minute of a journey is shown.

(a)   Calculate the acceleration of the
       vehicle in the first 10 seconds.
(b)   Calculate the total distance travelled
       by the vehicle in this minute.

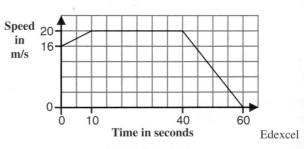

Edexcel

5 The diagram shows part of a speed-time graph of a motorcyclist's journey.
How long did the motorcyclist take to
travel the first 400 metres?

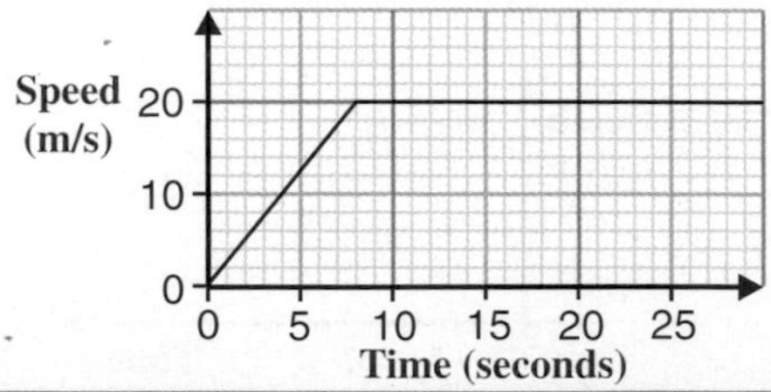

More or Less ●●●●●●●●●●●●

What you need to know

● **Inequalities** can be described using words or numbers and symbols.

Sign	Meaning
<	is less than
≤	is less than or equal to

Sign	Meaning
>	is greater than
≥	is greater than or equal to

● Inequalities can be shown on a **number line**.

Eg 1 This diagram shows the inequality: $-2 < x \leqslant 3$

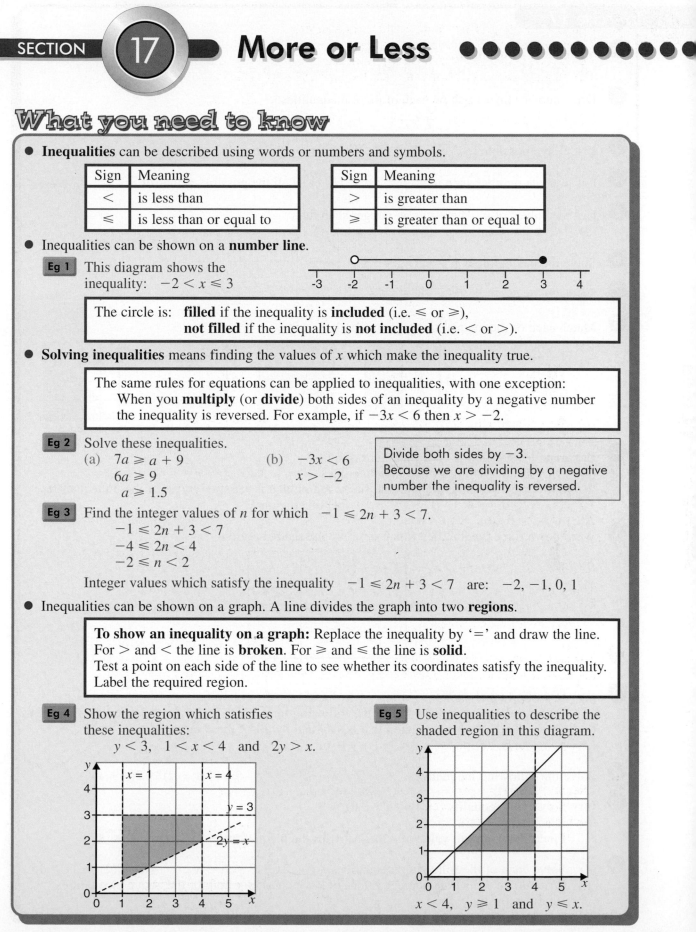

> The circle is: **filled** if the inequality is **included** (i.e. ≤ or ≥),
> **not filled** if the inequality is **not included** (i.e. < or >).

● **Solving inequalities** means finding the values of x which make the inequality true.

> The same rules for equations can be applied to inequalities, with one exception:
> When you **multiply** (or **divide**) both sides of an inequality by a negative number the inequality is reversed. For example, if $-3x < 6$ then $x > -2$.

Eg 2 Solve these inequalities.

(a) $7a \geqslant a + 9$
$6a \geqslant 9$
$a \geqslant 1.5$

(b) $-3x < 6$
$x > -2$

> Divide both sides by -3.
> Because we are dividing by a negative number the inequality is reversed.

Eg 3 Find the integer values of n for which $-1 \leqslant 2n + 3 < 7$.

$-1 \leqslant 2n + 3 < 7$
$-4 \leqslant 2n < 4$
$-2 \leqslant n < 2$

Integer values which satisfy the inequality $-1 \leqslant 2n + 3 < 7$ are: $-2, -1, 0, 1$

● Inequalities can be shown on a graph. A line divides the graph into two **regions**.

> **To show an inequality on a graph:** Replace the inequality by '=' and draw the line.
> For > and < the line is **broken**. For ≥ and ≤ the line is **solid**.
> Test a point on each side of the line to see whether its coordinates satisfy the inequality.
> Label the required region.

Eg 4 Show the region which satisfies these inequalities:
$y < 3$, $1 < x < 4$ and $2y > x$.

Eg 5 Use inequalities to describe the shaded region in this diagram.

$x < 4$, $y \geqslant 1$ and $y \leqslant x$.

1. Solve these inequalities.
   (a) $5x > 15$ (b) $x + 3 \geqslant 1$ (c) $2x \leqslant 6 - x$ (d) $3 - 2x > 7$

2. Draw number lines to show each of these inequalities.
   (a) $x \geqslant -2$ (b) $\frac{x}{3} < -1$ (c) $-1 < x \leqslant 3$ (d) $x \leqslant -1$ **and** $x > 3$

3. List all the possible integer values of n such that $-3 \leqslant n < 2$.   Edexcel

4. n is a whole number such that $6 < 2n < 13$. List all the possible values of n.   Edexcel

5. List the values of n, where n is an integer such that:
   (a) $-2 \leqslant 2n < 6$ (b) $-3 < n - 3 \leqslant -1$ (c) $-5 \leqslant 2n - 3 < 1$

6. Solve the inequalities.   (a) $2x - 5 > x + 2$ (b) $-9 < 5x + 1 \leqslant 6$

7. Solve the inequality $7y > 2y - 3$.   Edexcel

8. Match each of the inequalities to its **unshaded** region.

   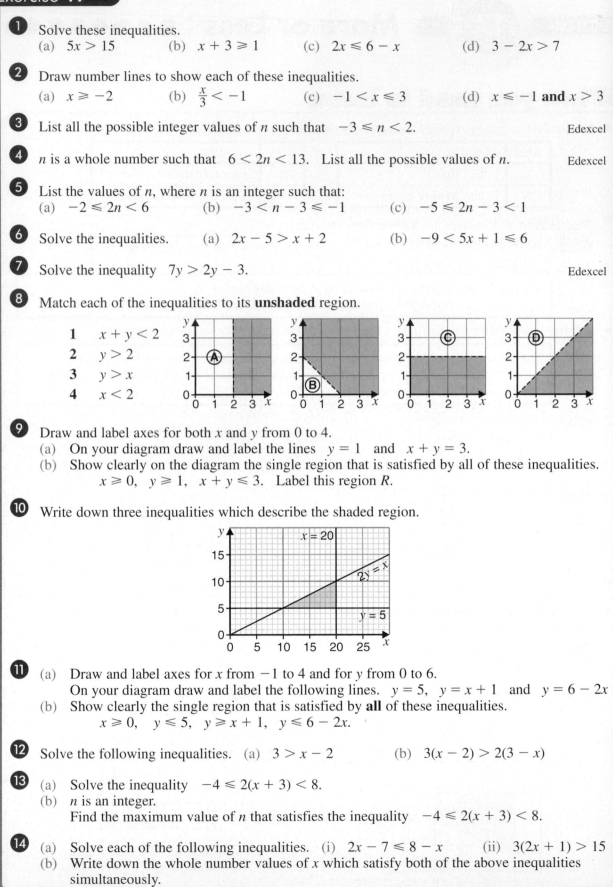

   1   $x + y < 2$
   2   $y > 2$
   3   $y > x$
   4   $x < 2$

9. Draw and label axes for both x and y from 0 to 4.
   (a) On your diagram draw and label the lines $y = 1$ and $x + y = 3$.
   (b) Show clearly on the diagram the single region that is satisfied by all of these inequalities.
        $x \geqslant 0$, $y \geqslant 1$, $x + y \leqslant 3$. Label this region R.

10. Write down three inequalities which describe the shaded region.

11. (a) Draw and label axes for x from -1 to 4 and for y from 0 to 6.
    On your diagram draw and label the following lines. $y = 5$, $y = x + 1$ and $y = 6 - 2x$
    (b) Show clearly the single region that is satisfied by **all** of these inequalities.
         $x \geqslant 0$, $y \leqslant 5$, $y \geqslant x + 1$, $y \leqslant 6 - 2x$.

12. Solve the following inequalities.   (a) $3 > x - 2$ (b) $3(x - 2) > 2(3 - x)$

13. (a) Solve the inequality $-4 \leqslant 2(x + 3) < 8$.
    (b) n is an integer.
    Find the maximum value of n that satisfies the inequality $-4 \leqslant 2(x + 3) < 8$.

14. (a) Solve each of the following inequalities.   (i) $2x - 7 \leqslant 8 - x$ (ii) $3(2x + 1) > 15$
    (b) Write down the whole number values of x which satisfy both of the above inequalities simultaneously.

Further Graphs

What you need to know

- The graph of a **linear function** is a straight line.
  The general equation of a straight line is $y = mx + c$.

- The graph of a **quadratic function** is always a smooth curve and is called a **parabola**.

- The general form of a **quadratic function** is
  $y = ax^2 + bx + c$, where a cannot be zero.
  The graph of a quadratic function is symmetrical
  and has a **maximum** or **minimum** value.

- The general form of a **cubic function** is $y = ax^3 + bx^2 + cx + d$, where a cannot be zero.

- The graph of the **reciprocal function** is of the
  form $y = \dfrac{a}{x}$, where x cannot be equal to zero.

  Eg 1

  $y = \dfrac{1}{x}$

- The graph of the **exponential function** is of the
  form $y = a^x$.

  Eg 2

  $y = 2^x$

- The graph of a **circle**, centre $(0, 0)$, is of the
  form $x^2 + y^2 = r^2$, where r is the radius
  of the circle.

  Eg 3

  $x^2 + y^2 = 16$

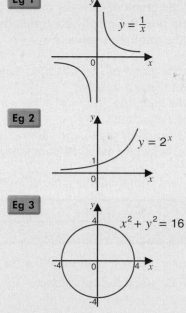

- The graph of a function can be used to solve a variety of equations.
  This may include drawing another graph and looking for points of intersection.

  Eg 4   (a)   Draw the graph of $y = x^2 - 2x - 5$ for values of x from -2 to 4.
        (b)   Use your graph to solve the equation $x^2 - 2x - 5 = 0$.

  (a)

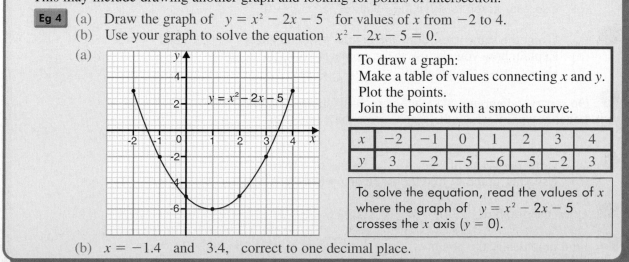

$y = x^2 - 2x - 5$

To draw a graph:
Make a table of values connecting x and y.
Plot the points.
Join the points with a smooth curve.

x	-2	-1	0	1	2	3	4
y	3	-2	-5	-6	-5	-2	3

To solve the equation, read the values of x
where the graph of $y = x^2 - 2x - 5$
crosses the x axis $(y = 0)$.

(b) $x = -1.4$ and   3.4,   correct to one decimal place.

1 Match these equations to their graphs. $y = 1 - x^2$ $y = x^2 - 1$

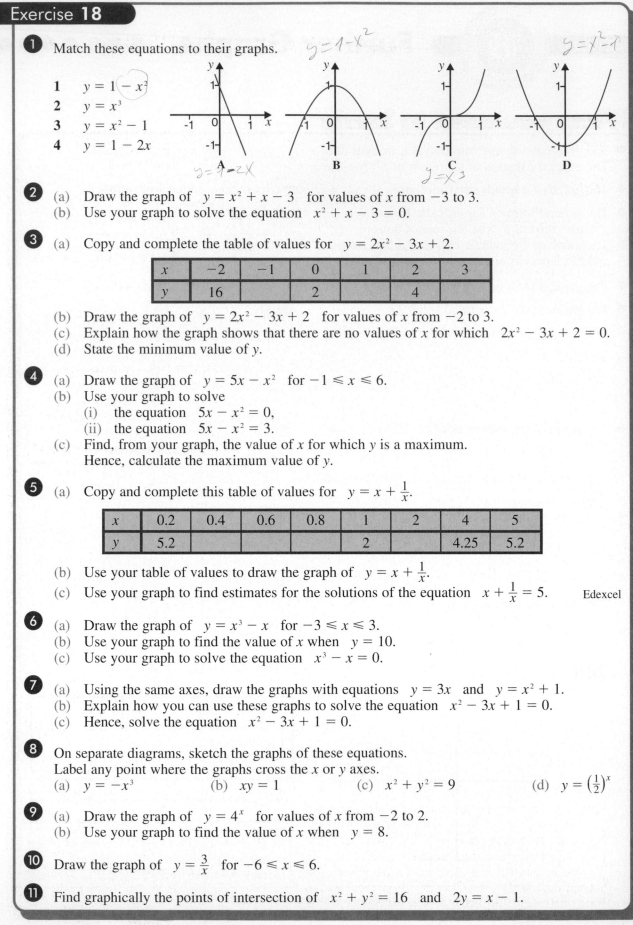

1. $y = 1 - x^2$
2. $y = x^3$
3. $y = x^2 - 1$
4. $y = 1 - 2x$

$y = 1 - 2x$ **A**   **B**   **C** $y = x^3$ **D**

2 (a) Draw the graph of $y = x^2 + x - 3$ for values of x from -3 to 3.
    (b) Use your graph to solve the equation $x^2 + x - 3 = 0$.

3 (a) Copy and complete the table of values for $y = 2x^2 - 3x + 2$.

x	-2	-1	0	1	2	3
y	16		2		4	

    (b) Draw the graph of $y = 2x^2 - 3x + 2$ for values of x from -2 to 3.
    (c) Explain how the graph shows that there are no values of x for which $2x^2 - 3x + 2 = 0$.
    (d) State the minimum value of y.

4 (a) Draw the graph of $y = 5x - x^2$ for $-1 \leqslant x \leqslant 6$.
    (b) Use your graph to solve
       (i)   the equation $5x - x^2 = 0$,
       (ii)   the equation $5x - x^2 = 3$.
    (c) Find, from your graph, the value of x for which y is a maximum.
       Hence, calculate the maximum value of y.

5 (a) Copy and complete this table of values for $y = x + \frac{1}{x}$.

x	0.2	0.4	0.6	0.8	1	2	4	5
y	5.2				2		4.25	5.2

    (b) Use your table of values to draw the graph of $y = x + \frac{1}{x}$.
    (c) Use your graph to find estimates for the solutions of the equation $x + \frac{1}{x} = 5$.   Edexcel

6 (a) Draw the graph of $y = x^3 - x$ for $-3 \leqslant x \leqslant 3$.
    (b) Use your graph to find the value of x when $y = 10$.
    (c) Use your graph to solve the equation $x^3 - x = 0$.

7 (a) Using the same axes, draw the graphs with equations $y = 3x$ and $y = x^2 + 1$.
    (b) Explain how you can use these graphs to solve the equation $x^2 - 3x + 1 = 0$.
    (c) Hence, solve the equation $x^2 - 3x + 1 = 0$.

8 On separate diagrams, sketch the graphs of these equations.
    Label any point where the graphs cross the x or y axes.
    (a) $y = -x^3$ (b) $xy = 1$ (c) $x^2 + y^2 = 9$ (d) $y = \left(\frac{1}{2}\right)^x$

9 (a) Draw the graph of $y = 4^x$ for values of x from -2 to 2.
    (b) Use your graph to find the value of x when $y = 8$.

10 Draw the graph of $y = \frac{3}{x}$ for $-6 \leqslant x \leqslant 6$.

11 Find graphically the points of intersection of $x^2 + y^2 = 16$ and $2y = x - 1$.

Quadratic Equations ● ● ● ● ● ●

What you need to know

● Brackets, such as $(x + 2)(x + 3)$, can be multiplied out using the **diagram method**, or by **expanding**.

Eg 1 Multiply out $(x + 2)(x + 3)$.

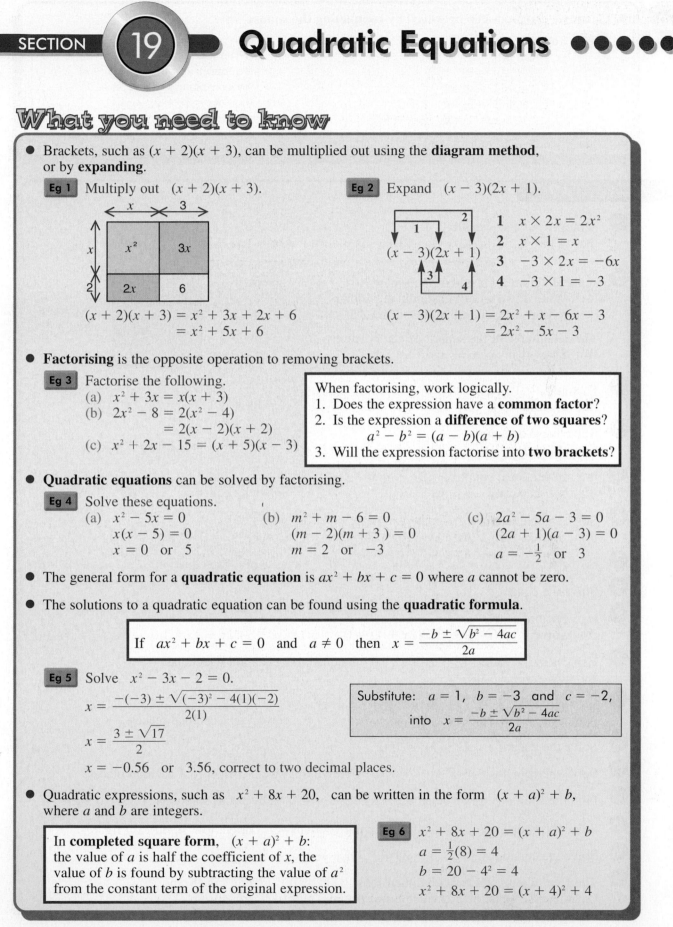

$(x + 2)(x + 3) = x^2 + 3x + 2x + 6$
$= x^2 + 5x + 6$

Eg 2 Expand $(x - 3)(2x + 1)$.

$(x - 3)(2x + 1)$

1   $x \times 2x = 2x^2$
2   $x \times 1 = x$
3   $-3 \times 2x = -6x$
4   $-3 \times 1 = -3$

$(x - 3)(2x + 1) = 2x^2 + x - 6x - 3$
$= 2x^2 - 5x - 3$

● **Factorising** is the opposite operation to removing brackets.

Eg 3 Factorise the following.
(a) $x^2 + 3x = x(x + 3)$
(b) $2x^2 - 8 = 2(x^2 - 4)$
     $= 2(x - 2)(x + 2)$
(c) $x^2 + 2x - 15 = (x + 5)(x - 3)$

When factorising, work logically.
1. Does the expression have a **common factor**?
2. Is the expression a **difference of two squares**?
    $a^2 - b^2 = (a - b)(a + b)$
3. Will the expression factorise into **two brackets**?

● **Quadratic equations** can be solved by factorising.

Eg 4 Solve these equations.
(a) $x^2 - 5x = 0$
    $x(x - 5) = 0$
    $x = 0$ or   5

(b) $m^2 + m - 6 = 0$
    $(m - 2)(m + 3) = 0$
    $m = 2$ or -3

(c) $2a^2 - 5a - 3 = 0$
    $(2a + 1)(a - 3) = 0$
    $a = -\frac{1}{2}$ or   3

● The general form for a **quadratic equation** is $ax^2 + bx + c = 0$ where a cannot be zero.

● The solutions to a quadratic equation can be found using the **quadratic formula**.

If $ax^2 + bx + c = 0$ and $a \neq 0$ then $x = \dfrac{-b \pm \sqrt{b^2 - 4ac}}{2a}$

Eg 5 Solve $x^2 - 3x - 2 = 0$.

$x = \dfrac{-(-3) \pm \sqrt{(-3)^2 - 4(1)(-2)}}{2(1)}$

$x = \dfrac{3 \pm \sqrt{17}}{2}$

$x = -0.56$ or   3.56, correct to two decimal places.

Substitute: $a = 1$, $b = -3$ and $c = -2$,
into $x = \dfrac{-b \pm \sqrt{b^2 - 4ac}}{2a}$

● Quadratic expressions, such as $x^2 + 8x + 20$, can be written in the form $(x + a)^2 + b$, where a and b are integers.

In **completed square form**, $(x + a)^2 + b$:
the value of a is half the coefficient of x, the
value of b is found by subtracting the value of a^2
from the constant term of the original expression.

Eg 6 $x^2 + 8x + 20 = (x + a)^2 + b$
$a = \frac{1}{2}(8) = 4$
$b = 20 - 4^2 = 4$
$x^2 + 8x + 20 = (x + 4)^2 + 4$

19

● Quadratic equations can be solved by **completing the square**.

Eg 7 Solve $x^2 + 4x = 5$.

$$(x + 2)^2 - 4 = 5$$
$$(x + 2)^2 = 9$$
$$x + 2 = \pm 3$$
$$x + 2 = 3 \quad \text{or} \quad x + 2 = -3$$
$$x = 1 \quad \text{or} \quad x = -5$$

> Write the left-hand side (LHS) of the equation in the form $(x + a)^2 + b$ by completing the square.
> $x^2 + 4x = (x + 2)^2 - 4$

● You should be able to form and solve quadratic equations.

Exercise 19

1 Multiply out and simplify.
(a) $x(x - 7)$ 　　(b) $(x - 2)(x + 5)$ 　　(c) $(2x - 1)(x + 3)$ 　　(d) $(3x + 2y)^2$

2 In the diagram each side of the square $ABCD$ is $(3 + x)$ cm.
(a) Write down an expression in terms of x for the area, in cm², of the square $ABCD$.

The actual area of the square $ABCD$ is 10 cm^2.
(b) Show that $x^2 + 6x = 1$.

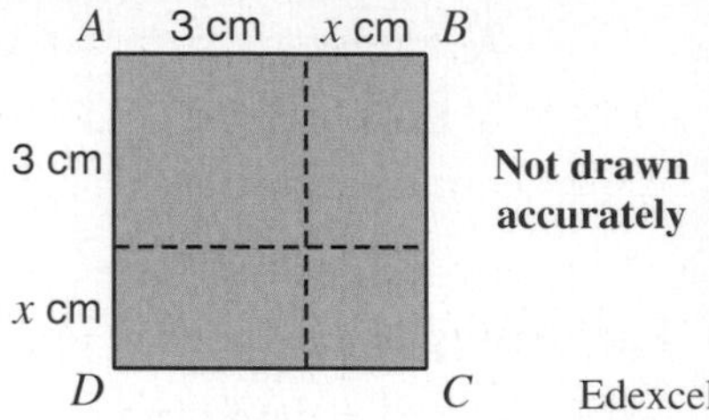

A　3 cm　x cm　B

3 cm

Not drawn accurately

x cm

D　　　　C　Edexcel

3 Factorise.
(a) $x^2 - 6x$ 　　(b) $x^2 + 2x - 15$ 　　(c) $x^2 - 4x + 3$ 　　(d) $x^2 - 9$

4 Solve these equations.
(a) $x(x + 5) = 0$ 　　(b) $(x - 3)(x + 2) = 0$ 　　(c) $(2x + 3)(x - 1) = 0$

5 (a) Expand and simplify $(2x - 5)(x + 3)$.
(b) (i) Factorise $x^2 + 6x - 7$. 　　(ii) Solve the equation $x^2 + 6x - 7 = 0$.
Edexcel

6 Solve these equations.
(a) $x^2 - 3x = 0$ 　(b) $x^2 - 3x + 2 = 0$ 　(c) $x^2 + x - 6 = 0$ 　(d) $x^2 - 11x + 28 = 0$

7 (a) Factorise $2x^2 - 5x - 3 = 0$. 　　(b) Hence, solve the equation $2x^2 - 5x - 3 = 0$.

8 Solve the equation $3x^2 - x - 2 = 0$.

9 (a) Factorise. (i) $2x^2 - 7x + 3$ 　　(ii) $4x^2 - 9$
(b) Solve. 　(i) $(3x + 2)(2x + 1) = 0$ 　(ii) $(3x + 2)(2x + 1) = 1$ 　Edexcel

10 Express in the form $x^2 + bx + c = 0$ the quadratic equation which has solutions $x = 2$ and $x = -3$.

11 (a) Write $x^2 - 4x - 8$ in the form $(x + a)^2 + b$.
(b) Hence, solve the equation $x^2 - 4x - 8 = 0$, correct to 2 decimal places.

12 Solve the equation $(2x - 3)^2 = 100$. 　Edexcel

13 Solve the equation $x^2 + 3x - 5 = 0$. Give your answers correct to 2 decimal places.

14 Find the solutions of the equation $x^2 - 4x - 1 = 0$. Give your solutions correct to 3 d.p.
Edexcel

15 Solve the equations $x^2 = 3x + 5$, giving your answers correct to 3 significant figures.

16 Solve the equation $2x^2 - x - 2 = 0$. Give your answer correct to 2 decimal places.

17 The area of a rectangle, with dimensions x cm by $(x + 2)$ cm, is 18 cm^2.
Calculate the value of x, correct to one decimal place.

Simultaneous Equations

What you need to know

- A pair of **simultaneous equations** has the same unknown letters in each equation.

- To solve a pair of simultaneous equations find values for the unknown letters that fit **both** equations.

- Simultaneous equations can be solved either **graphically** or **algebraically**.

- Solving simultaneous equations **graphically** involves:
    drawing the graphs of both equations,
    finding the point(s) where the graphs cross.
  When the graphs of both equations are parallel, the equations have no solution.

  Eg 1 Solve the simultaneous equations $x + 2y = 5$ and $x - 2y = 1$ graphically.

  Draw the graph of $x + 2y = 5$.
  Draw the graph of $x - 2y = 1$.

  The lines cross at the point (3, 1).
  This gives the solution $x = 3$ and $y = 1$.

- Solving simultaneous equations **algebraically** involves using either:
    the **elimination** method, or the **substitution** method.

  Eg 2 Solve the simultaneous equations $5x + 2y = 11$ and $3x - 4y = 4$ algebraically.

  $$5x + 2y = 11 \quad \text{A}$$
  $$3x - 4y = \ \ 4 \quad \text{B}$$

  A $\times$ 2 gives
  $$10x + 4y = 22 \quad \text{C}$$
  $$3x - 4y = \ \ 4 \quad \text{D}$$

  C + D gives
  $$13x = 26$$
  $$x = \ 2$$

  Substitute $x = 2$ into $5x + 2y = 11$.
  $$10 + 2y = 11$$
  $$2y = \ \ 1$$
  $$y = 0.5$$

  The solution is $x = 2$ and $y = 0.5$.

  > To make the number of y's the same we can multiply equation A by 2.

  > The number of y's is the **same** but the **signs** are **different**. To eliminate the y's the equations must be **added**.

  > You can check the solution by substituting $x = 2$ and $y = 0.5$ into $3x - 4y = 4$.

- You should be able to solve simultaneous equations in which one equation is linear and one is quadratic.

  Eg 3 Solve the simultaneous equations $y = x - 2$ and $x^2 + 3y = 12$.

  Substitute $y = x - 2$ into $x^2 + 3y = 12$.
  $$x^2 + 3(x - 2) = 12$$
  $$x^2 + 3x - 18 = 0$$
  $$(x + 6)(x - 3) = 0$$
  $$x = -6 \text{ or } x = 3$$

  Using $y = x - 2$.
  When $x = -6$.   When $x = 3$.
  $y = -6 - 2$ $y = 3 - 2$
  $y = -8$ $y = 1$

  This gives the solution: $x = -6$, $y = -8$ **and** $x = 3$, $y = 1$.

1 (a) On the same axes, draw the graphs of $y + x = 4$ and $y - 3x = 2$ for values of x from -2 to 2.
(b) Hence, solve the simultaneous equations $y + x = 4$ and $y - 3x = 2$.

2 Solve graphically the simultaneous equations $y = 3 - x$ and $y = x - 2$.

3 (a) On the same axes, draw the graphs of $x + y = 4$ and $y = x + 2$.
(b) Use the graphs to solve the simultaneous equations $x + y = 4$ and $y = x + 2$. *Edexcel*

4 The sketch shows the graph of $y = 2x - 1$.
Copy the diagram.

(a) On your diagram, sketch the graph of $y = 2x + 1$.
(b) Explain why the equations $y = 2x - 1$ and $y = 2x + 1$ cannot be solved simultaneously.

5 Solve these simultaneous equations. $6x + y = 7$
$2x - y = -3$

6 Solve the simultaneous equations $x + 3y = 13$ and $4x + 2y = 2$.

7 Solve the simultaneous equations. $3x + y = 13$
$2x - 3y = 16$ *Edexcel*

8 Heather sold 40 boxes of cards to raise money for charity.
She sold x small boxes at £4 each and y large boxes at £7 each.
She raised £184 altogether.
(a) Write down two equations connecting x and y.
(b) Solve these simultaneous equations to find how many of each size of box she sold.

9 Micro-scooters costs £x each and pogo sticks cost £y each.
2 micro-scooters and 4 pogo sticks cost £65.
1 micro-scooter and 3 pogo sticks cost £40.
(a) Write down two equations connecting x and y.
(b) Solve these simultaneous equations to find the cost of a micro-scooter and a pogo stick.

10 Solve these simultaneous equations. $2x + 5y = -1$ and $6x - y = 5$ *Edexcel*

11 Solve the simultaneous equations $2x + 3y = 7$ and $3x - 2y = 17$.

12 Use a graphical method to solve each of these pairs of simultaneous equations.
(a) $y = 4 - 2x$ (b) $y - x = 4$ (c) $y = 2x$
$y = x^2 - 4$ $y = 6x - x^2$ $x^2 + y^2 = 25$

13 Use an algebraic method to solve the simultaneous equations $5y = 2x - 7$ and $xy = 6$.

14 Solve the simultaneous equations.
(a) $y - x = -11$ (b) $y = 3 - x$ (c) $2x + y = 3$
$x^2 = y + 13$ $x^2 + y^2 = 17$ $y = \dfrac{1}{x}$

15 (a) Factorise $x^2 - 4y^2$.
(b) Solve the simultaneous equations. $x^2 - 4y^2 = 24$
$x + 2y = 6$ *Edexcel*

Algebraic Methods ● ● ● ● ● ●

What you need to know

- An **identity** is true for all values of x. It is the same expression written in another form.
  For example: $(2x + 3)^2 + (2x + 9)(2x + 5) = 2(4x^2 + 20x + 27)$.

  > To show that an identity is true, either:
  >   start with the LHS and show that it is equal to the RHS, or
  >   start with the RHS and show that it is equal to the LHS.

- **Algebraic fractions** have a numerator and a denominator.

  > To write an algebraic fraction in its **simplest form**:
  >   factorise the numerator and denominator of the fraction,
  >   divide the numerator and denominator by their highest
  >   common factor.

  Eg 1 Simplify.

  (a) $\dfrac{2x - 4}{x^2 - 2x} = \dfrac{2(x - 2)}{x(x - 2)} = \dfrac{2}{x}$

  (b) $\dfrac{x^2 - 9}{x^2 + 2x - 3} = \dfrac{(x + 3)(x - 3)}{(x + 3)(x - 1)} = \dfrac{(x - 3)}{(x - 1)}$

  (c) $\dfrac{2}{x - 3} - \dfrac{1}{x} = \dfrac{2x - (x - 3)}{x(x - 3)} = \dfrac{x + 3}{x(x - 3)}$

  > The same methods used for adding, subtracting, multiplying and
  > dividing numeric fractions can be applied to algebraic fractions.

- You should be able to solve equations involving algebraic fractions.

- The solutions to a variety of equations can be found using a process called **iteration**.

  Eg 2 Find a solution to the equation $x^2 - 4x - 3 = 0$,
  correct to 2 decimal places, using iteration.

  Use the iterative formula $x_{n + 1} = \sqrt{4x_n + 3}$.

  $x_1 = 4$

  $x_2 = \sqrt{4 \times 4 + 3} = 4.3588...$

  $x_3 = \sqrt{4 \times 4.3588... + 3} = 4.5205...$

  $x_4 = \sqrt{4 \times 4.5205... + 3} = 4.5915...$

  $x_5 = \sqrt{4 \times 4.5915... + 3} = 4.6223...$

  $x_6 = \sqrt{4 \times 4.6223... + 3} = 4.6356...$

  $x_7 = \sqrt{4 \times 4.6356... + 3} = 4.6414...$

  $x_8 = \sqrt{4 \times 4.6414... + 3} = 4.6438...$

  $x = 4.64$, correct to 2 d.p.

  > The process of iteration has three stages.
  >
  > 1. Rearranging an equation to form an **iterative formula**.
  >
  > 2. Choosing a **starting value**, x_1.
  >
  > 3. **Substituting** the starting value, and then values of x_n into the iterative formula.
  >
  > Continuing the process until the required degree of accuracy is obtained.

- **Trial and improvement** is a method used to solve equations. The accuracy of the value of the unknown letter is improved until the required degree of accuracy is obtained.

Eg 3 Use a trial and improvement method to find a solution to the equation $x^3 + x = 40$, correct to one decimal place.

x	$x^3 + x$	Comment
3	$27 + 3 = 30$	Too small
4	$64 + 4 = 68$	Too big
3.5	$42.8\ldots + 3.5 = 46.3\ldots$	Too big
3.3	$35.9\ldots + 3.3 = 39.2\ldots$	Too small
3.35	$37.5\ldots + 3.35 = 40.9\ldots$	Too big

For accuracy to 1 d.p.
check the second decimal place.
The solution lies between
3.3 and 3.35.

$x = 3.3$, correct to 1 d.p.

Exercise 21

1 Expand and simplify $(x + 3)^2 - (x - 3)^2$.

2 Show that $2x(x + y) - (x + y)^2 = x^2 - y^2$.

3 (a) By expanding both sides, or otherwise, show that
$$(m^2 + 1)(n^2 + 1) = (m + n)^2 + (mn - 1)^2.$$
(b) Using this result, or otherwise, write 500 050 as the sum of 2 square numbers.   Edexcel

4 Simplify. (a) $\dfrac{x^2 - 3x}{x}$ (b) $\dfrac{2x^2 - 6x}{4x - 12}$ (c) $\dfrac{x^2 + 2x + 1}{x^2 - 2x - 3}$ (d) $\dfrac{x^2 + x}{x^2 - 1}$

5 Simplify. (a) $\dfrac{1}{x} + \dfrac{1}{2x}$ (b) $\dfrac{2x}{x + 1} + \dfrac{1}{2}$ (c) $\dfrac{1}{x + 2} + \dfrac{2}{2x - 5}$

6 (a) Show that $y = \dfrac{3}{2x - 1} - \dfrac{2}{x + 3}$ can be written as $y = \dfrac{11 - x}{2x^2 + 5x - 3}$.
(b) Hence, find the values of x when $y = 1$.
Give your answers correct to 2 decimal places.

7 (a) Express $\dfrac{1}{x - 2} + \dfrac{2}{x + 4}$ as a single algebraic fraction.
(b) Hence, or otherwise, solve $\dfrac{1}{x - 2} + \dfrac{2}{x + 4} = \dfrac{1}{3}$.   Edexcel

8 Solve the equation $\dfrac{x}{2} - \dfrac{3}{x + 5} = 1$ correct to 2 decimal places.

9 Solve the equation $\dfrac{2}{2x - 1} - 1 = \dfrac{2}{x + 1}$.

10 (a) (i) Factorise $3x^2 - 8x - 3$. (ii) Hence, or otherwise, simplify $\dfrac{9x^2 - 1}{3x^2 - 8x - 3}$.
(b) Solve the equation $\dfrac{1}{1 - x} - \dfrac{1}{1 + x} = 1$.
Give your answer correct to two decimal places.

11 A solution to the equation $x^2 - 2x - 10 = 0$
may be found by using the iteration $x_{n + 1} = \sqrt{(2x_n + 10)}$.
(a) Starting with $x_1 = 4$, calculate x_2.
Write down all the figures on your calculator display.
(b) Continue this iteration until there is no change in the second decimal place.
Write down all the figures shown on your calculator for each value of x_n.   Edexcel

12 Use a trial and improvement method to solve the equation $x^3 + x^2 = 300$.
Show all your trials. Give your answer correct to one decimal place.

Transforming Graphs ●●●●●●

What you need to know

● **Function notation** is a way of expressing a relationship between two variables.
For example

Input, x ⟶ | function, f e.g. *cube* | ⟶ Output, f(x)

This notation gives f$(x) = x^3$

f(x) means 'a function of x'.
In the example above, f$(x) = x^3$ is equivalent to the equation $y = x^3$ where $y = $ f(x).

● **Transformations,** such as **translations** and **stretches**, can be used to change the position and size of a graph.
The equation of the transformed (new) graph is related to the equation of the original graph.

In general

Original	New graph	Transformation	Note
$y = $ f(x)	$y = $ f$(x) + a$	**translation**, vector $\begin{pmatrix} 0 \\ a \end{pmatrix}$.	If a is **positive**, curve moves a units **up**. If a is **negative**, curve moves a units **down**.
$y = $ f(x)	$y = $ f$(x + a)$	**translation**, vector $\begin{pmatrix} -a \\ 0 \end{pmatrix}$.	If a is **positive**, curve moves a units **left**. If a is **negative**, curve moves a units **right**.
$y = $ f(x)	$y = a$f(x)	**stretch**, from the x axis, parallel to the y axis, scale factor a.	The y coordinates on the graph of $y = $ f(x) are **multiplied** by a.
$y = $ f(x)	$y = $ f(ax)	**stretch**, from the y axis, parallel to the x axis, scale factor $\frac{1}{a}$.	The x coordinates on the graph of $y = $ f(x) are **divided** by a.
$y = $ f(x)	$y = -$f(x)	**reflection** in the x axis.	The y coordinates on the graph of $y = $ f(x) **change signs**.
$y = $ f(x)	$y = $ f$(-x)$	**reflection** in the y axis.	The x coordinates on the graph of $y = $ f(x) **change signs**.

Eg 1 The diagram shows the graph of $y = $ f(x).
Draw the graphs of $y = $ f$(x - 2)$ and $y = $ f$(x) - 2$.

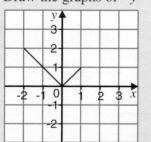
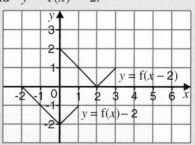

● You should be able to draw a suitable graph to find the relationship between a given set of variables.
Linear functions have straight line graphs, such as $y = ax + b$.
From the graph of **y against x**, the gradient $= a$ and the y-intercept $= b$.

Non-linear functions, such as $y = ax^n + b$, can be written as the linear function $y = az + b$
by substituting $z = x^n$.
From the graph of **y against x^n**, the gradient $= a$ and the y-intercept $= b$.

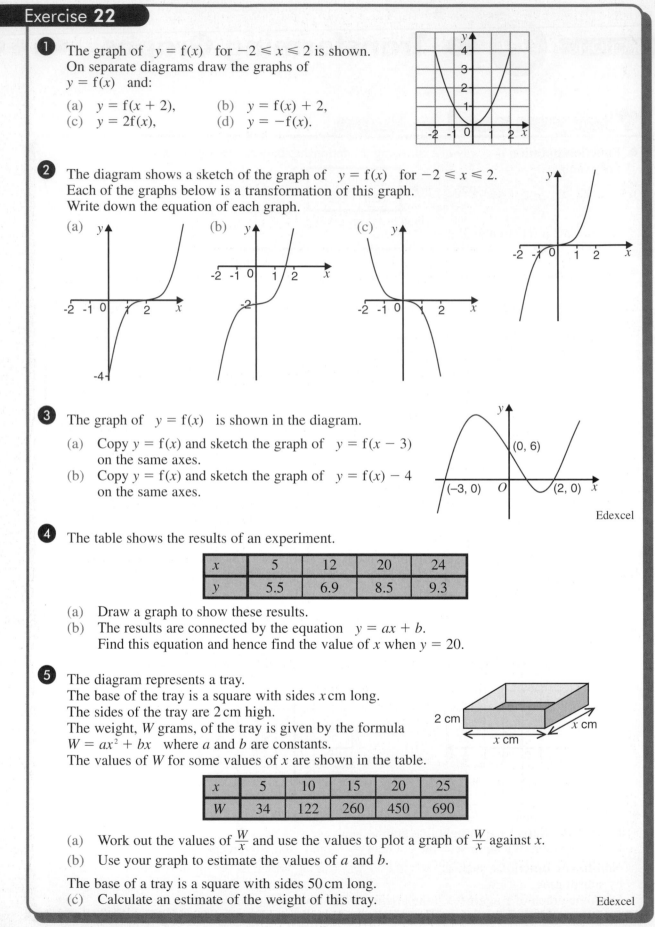

1 The graph of $y = f(x)$ for $-2 \leqslant x \leqslant 2$ is shown.
On separate diagrams draw the graphs of
$y = f(x)$ and:

(a) $y = f(x + 2)$,   (b) $y = f(x) + 2$,
(c) $y = 2f(x)$,   (d) $y = -f(x)$.

2 The diagram shows a sketch of the graph of $y = f(x)$ for $-2 \leqslant x \leqslant 2$.
Each of the graphs below is a transformation of this graph.
Write down the equation of each graph.

(a)   (b)   (c)

3 The graph of $y = f(x)$ is shown in the diagram.

(a) Copy $y = f(x)$ and sketch the graph of $y = f(x - 3)$
on the same axes.
(b) Copy $y = f(x)$ and sketch the graph of $y = f(x) - 4$
on the same axes.

(0, 6)

(-3, 0)   O   (2, 0) x

Edexcel

4 The table shows the results of an experiment.

x	5	12	20	24
y	5.5	6.9	8.5	9.3

(a) Draw a graph to show these results.
(b) The results are connected by the equation $y = ax + b$.
Find this equation and hence find the value of x when $y = 20$.

5 The diagram represents a tray.
The base of the tray is a square with sides x cm long.
The sides of the tray are 2 cm high.
The weight, W grams, of the tray is given by the formula
$W = ax^2 + bx$ where a and b are constants.
The values of W for some values of x are shown in the table.

2 cm x cm x cm

x	5	10	15	20	25
W	34	122	260	450	690

(a) Work out the values of $\dfrac{W}{x}$ and use the values to plot a graph of $\dfrac{W}{x}$ against x.

(b) Use your graph to estimate the values of a and b.

The base of a tray is a square with sides 50 cm long.
(c) Calculate an estimate of the weight of this tray.

Edexcel

Section Review - Algebra

1   (a)   Simplify   (i) $x + x + x$ (ii) $2a + 4b + a - 2b$ (iii) $3(a + 2)$
      (b)   Expand and simplify $2(x - 1) + 3(2x + 1)$
Edexcel

2   John uses this rule:
Think of a number, subtract 3 and then double the result.

John's answer is 8.
What number did he start with?

3   (a)   Copy and complete the table of values for $y = 3x - 2$.

x	-1	0	1	2	3
$y = 3x - 2$					

      (b)   Plot your values for x and y. Join your points with a straight line.
      (c)   Write down the coordinates of the point where your graph crosses the y axis.   Edexcel

4   Solve   (a) $x + 7 = 4$,   (b) $4x = 10$,   (c) $2x + 5 = 11$,   (d) $5 - 6x = 8$.

5   A sequence begins $1, \ -1, \ \ldots$
   This rule is used to continue the sequence.

Multiply the last number by 2 and then subtract 3.

      (a)   What is the next term in the sequence?
      (b)   A term in the sequence is called x.
           Write, in terms of x, the next term in the sequence.

6   The travel graph shows the journey of a
   train from Southampton to Winchester.
   Calculate the average speed of the train
   in miles per hour.

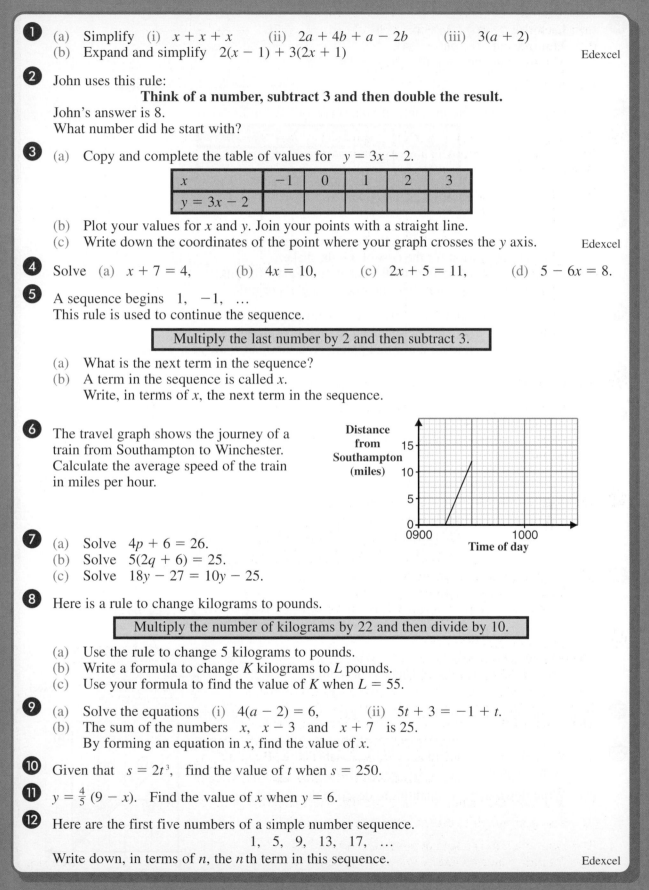

7   (a)   Solve $4p + 6 = 26$.
      (b)   Solve $5(2q + 6) = 25$.
      (c)   Solve $18y - 27 = 10y - 25$.

8   Here is a rule to change kilograms to pounds.

Multiply the number of kilograms by 22 and then divide by 10.

      (a)   Use the rule to change 5 kilograms to pounds.
      (b)   Write a formula to change K kilograms to L pounds.
      (c)   Use your formula to find the value of K when $L = 55$.

9   (a)   Solve the equations   (i) $4(a - 2) = 6$,   (ii) $5t + 3 = -1 + t$.
      (b)   The sum of the numbers $x, \ \ x - 3$ and $x + 7$ is 25.
           By forming an equation in x, find the value of x.

10   Given that $s = 2t^3$,   find the value of t when $s = 250$.

11 $y = \frac{4}{5}(9 - x)$.   Find the value of x when $y = 6$.

12   Here are the first five numbers of a simple number sequence.
$1, \ \ 5, \ \ 9, \ \ 13, \ \ 17, \ \ \ldots$

   Write down, in terms of n, the nth term in this sequence.   Edexcel

13 (a) On the same diagram draw the graphs $2y = x + 4$ and $y = \frac{1}{2}x + 1$.
   (b) What do you notice about the two lines you have drawn?

14 (a) Factorise   (i) $3a - 6$,   (ii) $k^2 - 2k$.
   (b) Multiply out   (i) $m(m - 4)$,   (ii) $3x(x + 5)$.
   (c) Multiply out and simplify $2(5x - 3) - 3(x - 1)$.

   (d) Solve   (i) $\dfrac{3x + 5}{2} = 7$,   (ii) $3 - 4x = x + 8$,   (iii) $3(2x + 1) = 6$.

15 (a) Copy and complete the table of values for $y = x^2 - 3$.

x	-2	-1	0	1	2	3
y		-2	-3			6

   (b) Draw the graph of $y = x^2 - 3$ for values of x from -2 to 3.
   (c) Use your graph to solve the equation $x^2 - 3 = 0$.

16 A glass of milk costs x pence.
   A milk shake costs 45 pence more than a glass of milk.
   (a) Write an expression for the cost of a milk shake.
   (b) Lou has to pay £4.55 for 3 milk shakes and a glass of milk.
       By forming an equation, find the price of a glass of milk.

17 A solution of the equation $x^3 - 9x = 5$ is between 3 and 4.
   Use the method of trial and improvement to find this solution.
   Give your answer correct to 2 decimal places. You must show **all** your working.   Edexcel

18 (a) Solve the inequality $3x < 6 - x$.
   (b) List all the values of n, where n is an integer, such that $-3 < 2x + 1 \leqslant 3$.

19 Match these equations to their graphs.

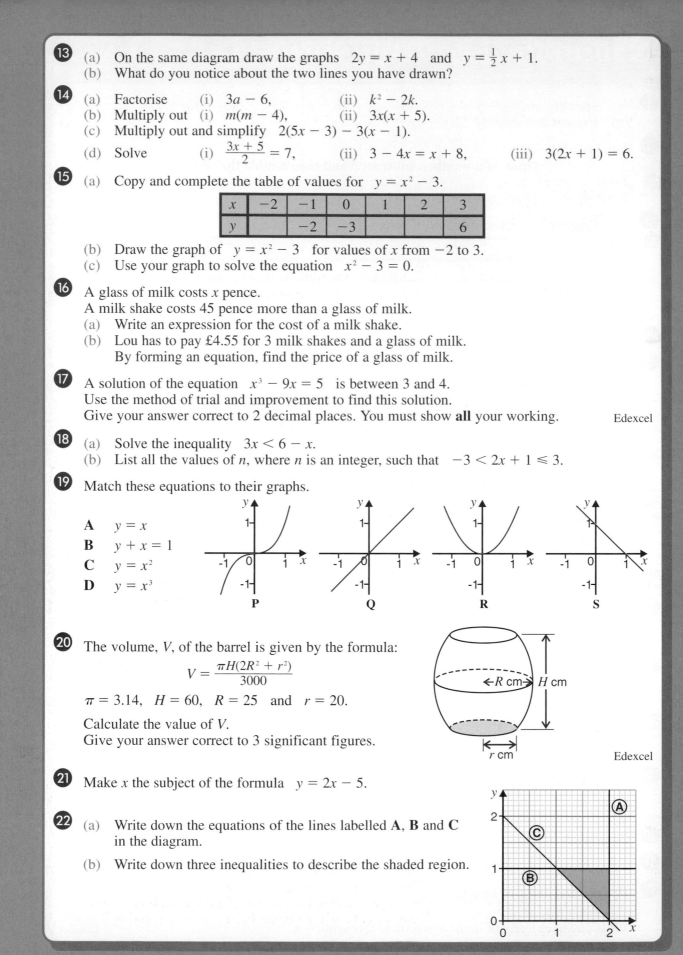

A $y = x$
B $y + x = 1$
C $y = x^2$
D $y = x^3$

     P   Q   R   S

20 The volume, V, of the barrel is given by the formula:
$$V = \frac{\pi H(2R^2 + r^2)}{3000}$$

   $\pi = 3.14$, $H = 60$, $R = 25$ and $r = 20$.

   Calculate the value of V.
   Give your answer correct to 3 significant figures.   Edexcel

21 Make x the subject of the formula $y = 2x - 5$.

22 (a) Write down the equations of the lines labelled **A**, **B** and **C**
       in the diagram.

   (b) Write down three inequalities to describe the shaded region.

23 Solve the equation $\dfrac{5x-3}{3} - \dfrac{1+2x}{2} = 3$

24 (a) Draw the graph of $y = x^2 - 2x + 1$ for values of x from -1 to 3.
(b) Use your graph to solve the equation $x^2 - 2x + 1 = 0$.
(c) Use your graph to solve the equation $x^2 - 2x + 1 = 2$.

25 (a) Work out the value of $x^2 - 5x + 6$ when $x = -2$.
(b) (i) Factorise $x^2 - 5x + 6$. (ii) Hence, solve the equation $x^2 - 5x + 6 = 0$.

26 (a) Factorise (i) $2st - 4t$, (ii) $3y^2 + 6y$, (iii) $d^2 - 2d - 24$.
(b) Solve the equations (i) $x(x + 2) = 0$, (ii) $y^2 - 3y + 2 = 0$.
(c) Expand and simplify $(2x - 3)(x + 2)$.

27 $v = u - ft$
(a) Express t in terms of u, v and f.
(b) When $u = 10$ and $v = 2$, write down the formula for t in terms of f.
(c) Given that $1 \leqslant f \leqslant 10$, and that t is a **whole number**, use your answer to (b) to write down all the possible values of t.

Edexcel

28 The line with equation $3y = -2x + 6$ has been drawn on the grid.
(a) Copy the diagram and draw the graph of $y = 2x - 2$ on the same grid.
(b) Use the graphs to find the solution of the simultaneous equations $3y = -2x + 6$ and $y = 2x - 2$.
A line is drawn parallel to $3y = -2x + 6$ through the point $(2, 1)$.
(c) Find the equation of this line.

Edexcel

29 (a) Expand $x(x + 4)$.
(b) Solve the simultaneous equations $x + 8y = 5$ and $3x - 4y = 8$.

Edexcel

30 (a) Simplify. (i) $\dfrac{p^6}{p^2}$ (ii) $q^3 \times q$ (iii) $(x^3)^2$
(b) Simplify (i) $3a^2 \times 2a^2b^3$, (ii) $(2a^2)^{-3}$.
(c) Factorise completely $9x^2y - 6xy^3$.

Edexcel

31

The graph of a function has been sketched for $0 < x \leqslant 10$.
The equation of the function is **one** of the following:

$$y = kx^3 \quad \textbf{or} \quad y = kx^2 \quad \textbf{or} \quad y = \dfrac{k}{x}$$

where k is a positive constant.
By choosing the appropriate equation and using the point $(6, 2)$ which lies on the curve, calculate the value of k.

Edexcel

32 (a) The graph of a straight line is shown.
What is the equation of the line?

(b) The equation of a different line is $4y - 3x = 8$.
What is the gradient of this line?

33 (a) Simplify $\dfrac{x^2 - 3x}{3x - 9}$. (b) Factorise fully $3x^2 - 12$. (c) Solve $x^2 + 3x - 10 = 0$.

34

The dimensions of a rectangle are shown.
The rectangle has an area of 104 cm^2.
Form an equation for the area of the rectangle and show that it can be written in the form $2x^2 + x - 105 = 0$.

35 You are given the formula $y = \sqrt{\frac{2x}{5}}$.

   (a)   Find the value of y when $x = 3.6 \times 10^{-4}$

   (b)   Rearrange the formula to give x in terms of y.

36 The diagram shows points $A(2, 0)$, $B(0, 2)$ and $C(3, 5)$.

   Find the equations of the line segments.

   (a) AB,   (b) BC,   (c) AC.

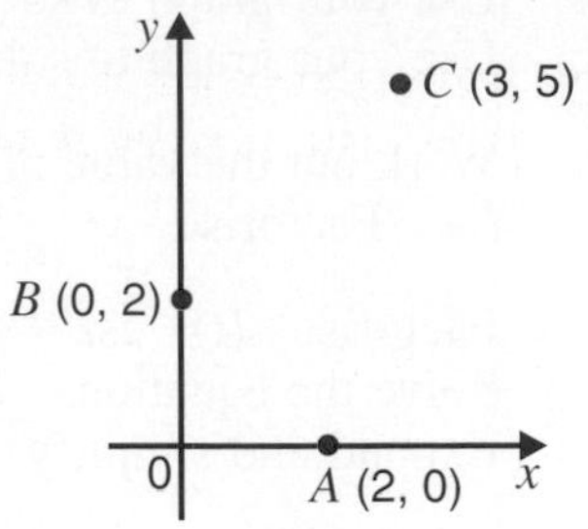

37 Simplify.   (a) $(3x^2y)^3$ (b) $\dfrac{3a^2b^3 \times 4a^5b}{6a^3b^2}$

38 Factorise the following.   (a) $3x^2 - 75$ (b) $3x^2 - 8x + 5$

39 Solve the equation $x^2 + 2x - 5 = 0$.
   Give your answers correct to two decimal places.

40 The volumes of these cuboids are the same.

   (a)   Show that $3x^2 + 2x - 12 = 0$.

   (b)   By solving the equation
         $3x^2 + 2x - 12 = 0$ find the value of x.
         Give your answer correct to one decimal place.

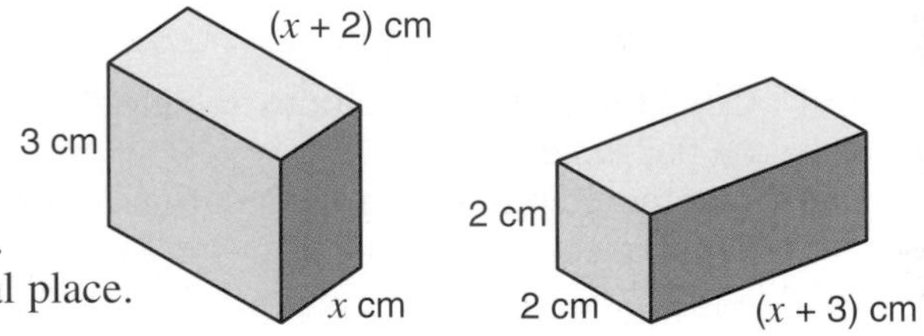

41 On separate diagrams, sketch the graphs of:

   (a) $x^2 + y^2 = 9$,   (b) $y = 2^x$,   for $-3 \leqslant x \leqslant 3$.

42 y is directly proportional to the square root of x.   When $x = 25$ then $y = 15$.

   (a)   Work out a formula to connect x and y.

   (b)   Work out the value of x when $y = 6$.

   Edexcel

43 (a)   Show that $(2x + 3)^2 - (2x + 1)^2 = 8(x + 1)$.

   (b)   Hence, solve the equation $(2x + 3)^2 - (2x + 1)^2 = x^2 - 1$.

44 Rearrange the equation $x = \dfrac{y - 5}{3 - y}$ to make y the subject.

45 The speed-time graph of an underground train
   travelling between two stations is shown.

   (a)   What is the maximum speed of the train?

   (b)   Calculate the acceleration of the train.

   (c)   Calculate the distance between the stations.

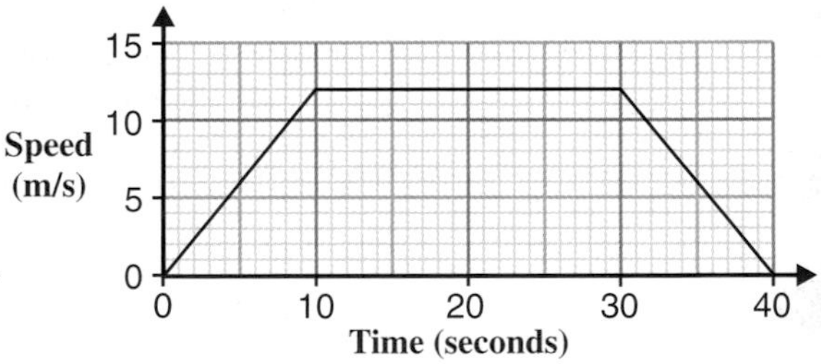

46 Find the equation of the line which is perpendicular to $2y + x = 6$
   and goes through the point $(4, 1)$.

47 Solve the equation $2x^2 = 5x - 1$.
   Give your answers correct to two decimal places.

48 (a)   Draw the graph of $y = \dfrac{2}{x}$ for $0 \leqslant x \leqslant 8$.

   (b)   On the same diagram draw the graph of $3y = 13 - 2x$.

   The equation $3y = 13 - 2x$ can be written as $y = 4\frac{1}{3} - \frac{2}{3}x$.

   (c)   Show that $\dfrac{2}{x} = 4\frac{1}{3} - \frac{2}{3}x$ can be written as $2x^2 - 13x + 6 = 0$.

   (d)   Use your graphs, or otherwise, to solve the equation $2x^2 - 13x + 6 = 0$.

49 Here is the graph of $y = f(x)$.

(a) Copy the graph of $y = f(x)$ and sketch the graph of $y = f(x + 2)$ on the same axes.

(b) Copy the graph of $y = f(x)$ and sketch the graph of $y = 2f(x)$ on the same axes.

Edexcel

50 (a) Factorise $p^2 - q^2$.

Here is a sequence of numbers: 0, 3, 8, 15, 24, 35, 48, …
(b) Write down an expression for the nth term of this sequence.
(c) Show algebraically that the product of **any** two consecutive terms of the sequence

$$0, \ 3, \ 8, \ 15, \ 24, \ 35, \ 48, \ …$$

can be written as the product of four consecutive integers.

Edexcel

51 You are given that $y = 8x^n$ and that $y = 1$ when $x = 2$. Find the value of n.

52 (a) Simplify fully the expression $\dfrac{2x^2 - 18}{2x^2 - 4x - 6}$.

(b) You are given the equation $xy = x + y$.
Rearrange the equation to give a formula for y in terms of x.

(c) You are given that $(2x - b)^2 - 5 = ax^2 - 4x + c$ for all values of x.
Find the values of a, b and c.

53 Solve the simultaneous equations $x + y = 4$ and $y = x^2 + 2x$.

54 A solution of $x^3 + x^2 - 4 = 0$ may be found by using the iteration $x_{n+1} = \dfrac{2}{\sqrt{(x_n + 1)}}$.

(a) Use $x_1 = 1$ to calculate x_2. Write down all the figures on your calculator display.
(b) Continue with this iteration until you find a solution of $x^3 + x^2 - 4 = 0$ correct to 2 decimal places. Write down all the figures on your calculator display for each value of x_n which you need to find.

Edexcel

55 The curve $y = a + bx - x^2$ passes through the points $P(1, 6)$ and $Q(2, 6)$.
Find the equation of the curve and hence find the points at which the curve crosses the x axis.

56 Solve the equation $\dfrac{2}{x-1} - \dfrac{1}{x+1} = 1$. Give your answers correct to 2 decimal places.

57 A transformation has been applied to the graph of $y = x^2$ to give the graph of $y = -x^2$.
(a) Describe fully the transformation.

For all values of x, $x^2 + 4x = (x + p)^2 + q$.
(b) Find the values of p and q.

A transformation has been applied to the graph of $y = x^2$ to give the graph of $y = x^2 + 4x$.
(c) Using your answer to part (b), or otherwise, describe fully the transformation.

Edexcel

58 Solve the simultaneous equations $y = 2x + 1$ and $xy = 3$.

59 You are given that $\dfrac{1}{x+1} - \dfrac{3}{2x-1} = 2$.
Show that $4x^2 + 3x + 2 = 0$.

Section Review · · · Section Review · · · Section Review

Angles, Parallel Lines and Polygons

What you need to know

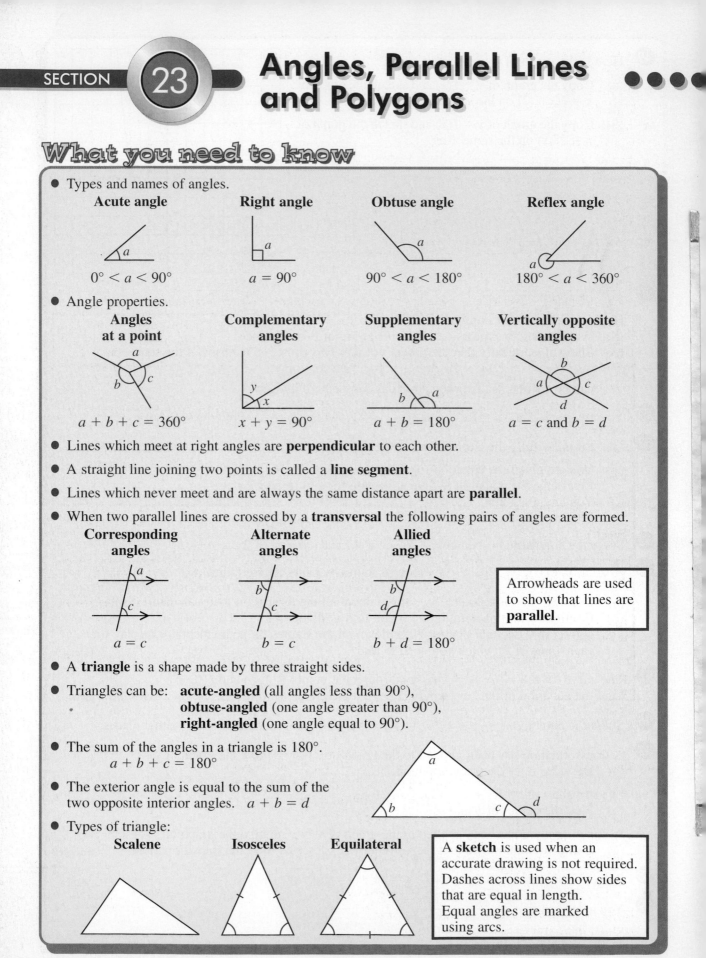

- Types and names of angles.

Acute angle	Right angle	Obtuse angle	Reflex angle
$0° < a < 90°$	$a = 90°$	$90° < a < 180°$	$180° < a < 360°$

- Angle properties.

Angles at a point	Complementary angles	Supplementary angles	Vertically opposite angles
$a + b + c = 360°$	$x + y = 90°$	$a + b = 180°$	$a = c$ and $b = d$

- Lines which meet at right angles are **perpendicular** to each other.

- A straight line joining two points is called a **line segment**.

- Lines which never meet and are always the same distance apart are **parallel**.

- When two parallel lines are crossed by a **transversal** the following pairs of angles are formed.

Corresponding angles	Alternate angles	Allied angles
$a = c$	$b = c$	$b + d = 180°$

Arrowheads are used to show that lines are **parallel**.

- A **triangle** is a shape made by three straight sides.

- Triangles can be: **acute-angled** (all angles less than 90°),
  obtuse-angled (one angle greater than 90°),
  right-angled (one angle equal to 90°).

- The sum of the angles in a triangle is 180°.
  $$a + b + c = 180°$$

- The exterior angle is equal to the sum of the two opposite interior angles. $a + b = d$

- Types of triangle:

Scalene   Isosceles   Equilateral

A **sketch** is used when an accurate drawing is not required. Dashes across lines show sides that are equal in length. Equal angles are marked using arcs.

- A two-dimensional shape has **line symmetry** if the line divides the shape so that one side fits exactly over the other.

- A two-dimensional shape has **rotational symmetry** if it fits into a copy of its outline as it is rotated through 360°.

- A shape is only described as having rotational symmetry if the order of rotational symmetry is 2 or more.

- The number of times a shape fits into its outline in a single turn is the **order of rotational symmetry**.

Order of rotational symmetry 5

- A **quadrilateral** is a shape made by four straight lines.

- The sum of the angles in a quadrilateral is 360°.

- Facts about these special quadrilaterals:

parallelogram   rectangle   square   rhombus   trapezium   isosceles trapezium   kite

Quadrilateral	Sides	Angles	Diagonals	Line symmetry	Order of rotational symmetry	Area formula
Parallelogram	Opposite sides equal and parallel	Opposite angles equal	Bisect each other	0	2	$A = bh$
Rectangle	Opposite sides equal and parallel	All 90°	Bisect each other	2	2	$A = bh$
Rhombus	4 equal sides, opposite sides parallel	Opposite angles equal	Bisect each other at 90°	2	2	$A = bh$
Square	4 equal sides, opposite sides parallel	All 90°	Bisect each other at 90°	4	4	$A = l^2$
Trapezium	1 pair of parallel sides					$A = \frac{1}{2}(a + b)\,h$
Isosceles trapezium	1 pair of parallel sides, non-parallel sides equal	2 pairs of equal angles	Equal in length	1	1*	$A = \frac{1}{2}(a + b)\,h$
Kite	2 pairs of adjacent sides equal	1 pair of opposite angles equal	One bisects the other at 90°	1	1*	

*A shape is only described as having rotational symmetry if the order of rotational symmetry is 2 or more.

- A **polygon** is a many-sided shape made by straight lines.

- A polygon with all sides equal and all angles equal is called a **regular polygon**.

- Shapes you need to know: A 5-sided polygon is called a **pentagon**.
  A 6-sided polygon is called a **hexagon**.
  An 8-sided polygon is called an **octagon**.

- The sum of the exterior angles of any polygon is 360°.

- At each vertex of a polygon: interior angle + exterior angle = 180°

- The sum of the interior angles of an n-sided polygon is given by:
  $(n - 2) \times 180°$

interior angle   exterior angle

- For a regular n-sided polygon: exterior angle = $\frac{360°}{n}$

- A shape will **tessellate** if it covers a surface without overlapping and leaves no gaps.

Angles, Parallel Lines and Polygons

The diagrams in this exercise have not been drawn accurately.

1 Find the size of the lettered angles. Give a reason for each answer.

(a)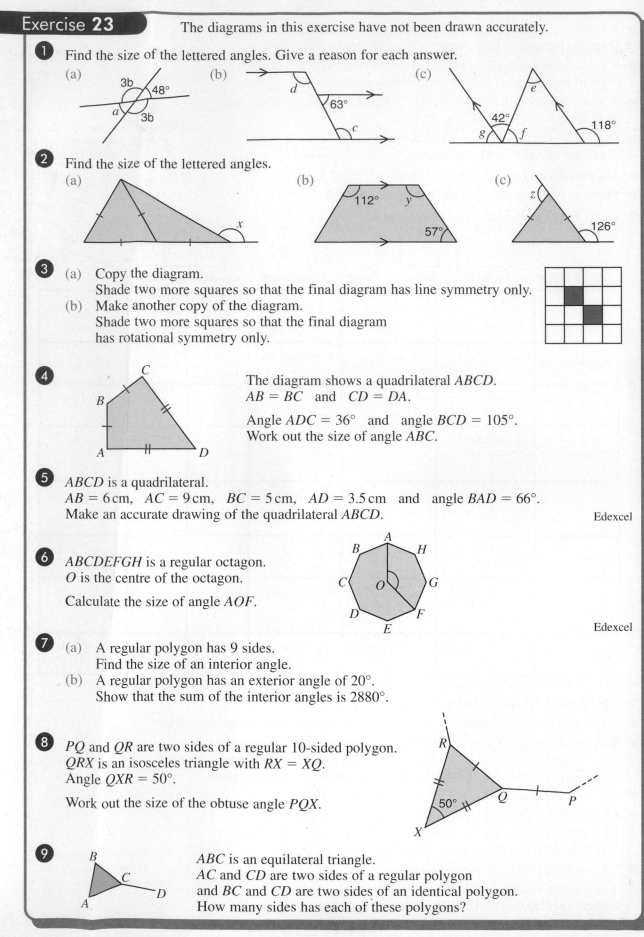

(b)

(c)

2 Find the size of the lettered angles.

(a)

(b)

(c)

3 (a) Copy the diagram.
Shade two more squares so that the final diagram has line symmetry only.
(b) Make another copy of the diagram.
Shade two more squares so that the final diagram
has rotational symmetry only.

4

The diagram shows a quadrilateral $ABCD$.
$AB = BC$ and $CD = DA$.

Angle $ADC = 36°$ and   angle $BCD = 105°$.
Work out the size of angle ABC.

5 $ABCD$ is a quadrilateral.
$AB = 6$ cm, $AC = 9$ cm, $BC = 5$ cm, $AD = 3.5$ cm   and   angle $BAD = 66°$.
Make an accurate drawing of the quadrilateral $ABCD$.

Edexcel

6 $ABCDEFGH$ is a regular octagon.
O is the centre of the octagon.

Calculate the size of angle AOF.

Edexcel

7 (a) A regular polygon has 9 sides.
Find the size of an interior angle.
(b) A regular polygon has an exterior angle of $20°$.
Show that the sum of the interior angles is $2880°$.

8 PQ and QR are two sides of a regular 10-sided polygon.
QRX is an isosceles triangle with $RX = XQ$.
Angle $QXR = 50°$.

Work out the size of the obtuse angle PQX.

9 ABC is an equilateral triangle.
AC and CD are two sides of a regular polygon
and BC and CD are two sides of an identical polygon.
How many sides has each of these polygons?

Circle Properties

What you need to know

- A **circle** is the shape drawn by keeping a pencil the same distance from a fixed point on a piece of paper.

- You should know the meaning of the words shown on the diagrams below.

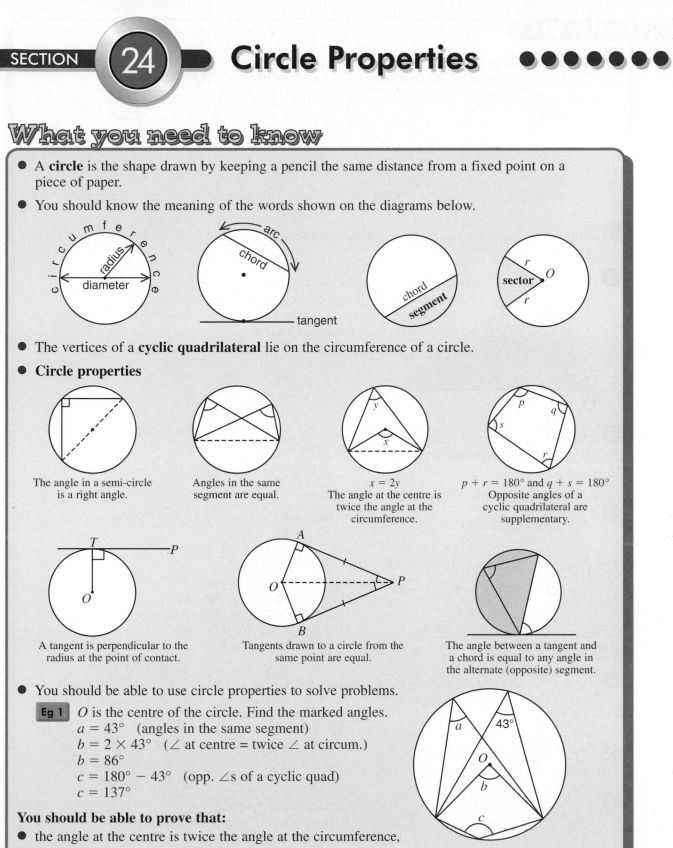

- The vertices of a **cyclic quadrilateral** lie on the circumference of a circle.

- **Circle properties**

The angle in a semi-circle is a right angle.

Angles in the same segment are equal.

$x = 2y$
The angle at the centre is twice the angle at the circumference.

$p + r = 180°$ and $q + s = 180°$
Opposite angles of a cyclic quadrilateral are supplementary.

A tangent is perpendicular to the radius at the point of contact.

Tangents drawn to a circle from the same point are equal.

The angle between a tangent and a chord is equal to any angle in the alternate (opposite) segment.

- You should be able to use circle properties to solve problems.

Eg 1 O is the centre of the circle. Find the marked angles.
$a = 43°$ (angles in the same segment)
$b = 2 × 43°$ ($\angle$ at centre = twice $\angle$ at circum.)
$b = 86°$
$c = 180° - 43°$ (opp. $\angle$s of a cyclic quad)
$c = 137°$

You should be able to prove that:

- the angle at the centre is twice the angle at the circumference,
- the angle in a semi-circle is a right angle,
- angles in the same segment are equal,
- opposite angles of a cyclic quadrilateral are supplementary,
- the angle between a tangent and a chord is equal to any angle in the alternate segment.

The diagrams in this exercise have not been drawn accurately.

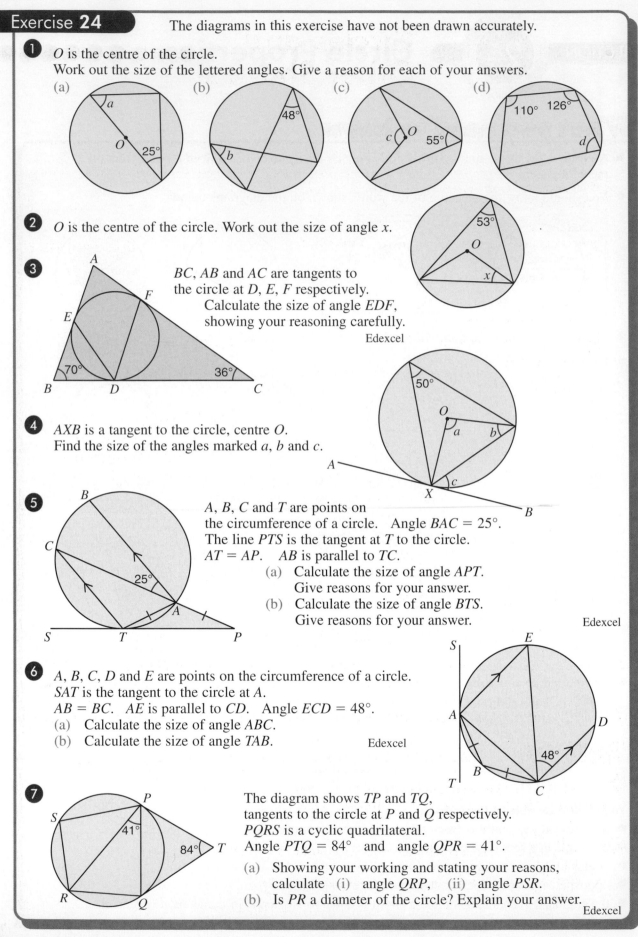

1 *O* is the centre of the circle.
Work out the size of the lettered angles. Give a reason for each of your answers.

(a)   (b)   (c)   (d)

2 *O* is the centre of the circle. Work out the size of angle *x*.

3 *BC*, *AB* and *AC* are tangents to
the circle at *D*, *E*, *F* respectively.
Calculate the size of angle *EDF*,
showing your reasoning carefully.
Edexcel

4 *AXB* is a tangent to the circle, centre *O*.
Find the size of the angles marked *a*, *b* and *c*.

5 *A*, *B*, *C* and *T* are points on
the circumference of a circle.   Angle *BAC* = 25°.
The line *PTS* is the tangent at *T* to the circle.
AT = *AP*.   *AB* is parallel to *TC*.
(a)   Calculate the size of angle *APT*.
Give reasons for your answer.
(b)   Calculate the size of angle *BTS*.
Give reasons for your answer.
Edexcel

6 *A*, *B*, *C*, *D* and *E* are points on the circumference of a circle.
SAT is the tangent to the circle at *A*.
AB = *BC*.   *AE* is parallel to *CD*.   Angle *ECD* = 48°.
(a)   Calculate the size of angle *ABC*.
(b)   Calculate the size of angle *TAB*.   Edexcel

7 The diagram shows *TP* and *TQ*,
tangents to the circle at *P* and *Q* respectively.
PQRS is a cyclic quadrilateral.
Angle *PTQ* = 84°   and   angle *QPR* = 41°.
(a)   Showing your working and stating your reasons,
calculate   (i) angle *QRP*,   (ii) angle *PSR*.
(b)   Is *PR* a diameter of the circle? Explain your answer.
Edexcel

Circles and Other Shapes

●●●●●●●●●●●●

What you need to know

● You should be able to calculate **lengths** and **areas** associated with **circles**.

Circumference of a circle is given by: $C = \pi d$ or $C = 2\pi r$
Area of a circle is given by: $A = \pi r^2$

The **lengths of arcs** and the **areas of sectors** are proportional to the angle at the centre of the circle.
For a sector with angle $a°$

$$\text{Length of arc} = \frac{a}{360} \times \pi d$$

$$\text{Area of sector} = \frac{a}{360} \times \pi r^2$$

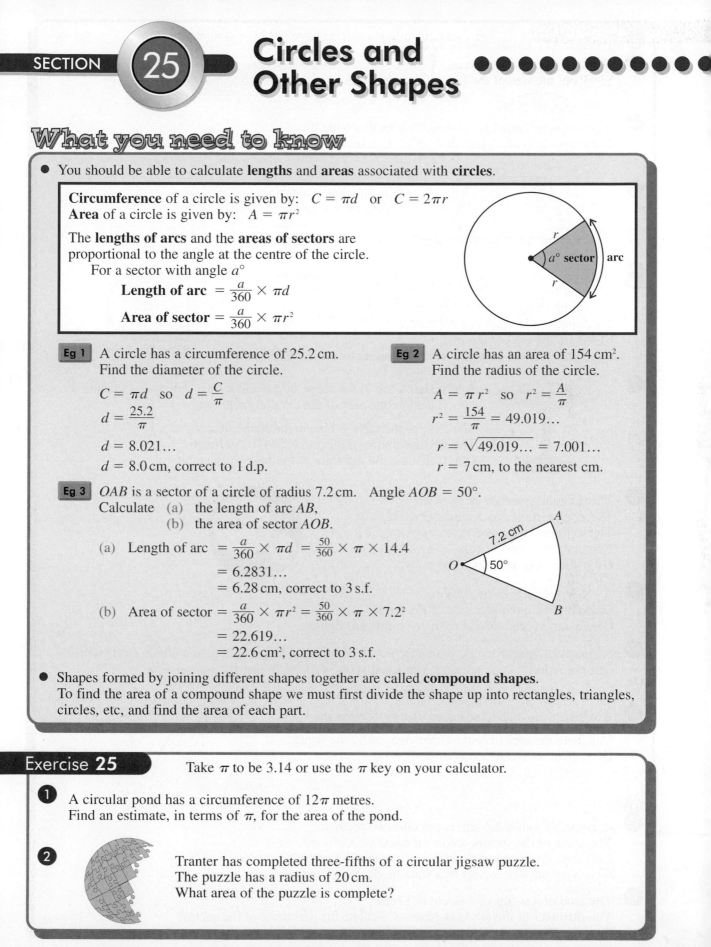

Eg 1 A circle has a circumference of 25.2 cm.
Find the diameter of the circle.

$C = \pi d$ so $d = \dfrac{C}{\pi}$

$d = \dfrac{25.2}{\pi}$

$d = 8.021...$

$d = 8.0$ cm, correct to 1 d.p.

Eg 2 A circle has an area of 154 cm².
Find the radius of the circle.

$A = \pi r^2$ so $r^2 = \dfrac{A}{\pi}$

$r^2 = \dfrac{154}{\pi} = 49.019...$

$r = \sqrt{49.019...} = 7.001...$

$r = 7$ cm, to the nearest cm.

Eg 3 OAB is a sector of a circle of radius 7.2 cm. Angle $AOB = 50°$.
Calculate (a) the length of arc AB,
(b) the area of sector AOB.

(a) Length of arc $= \dfrac{a}{360} \times \pi d = \dfrac{50}{360} \times \pi \times 14.4$

$= 6.2831...$

$= 6.28$ cm, correct to 3 s.f.

(b) Area of sector $= \dfrac{a}{360} \times \pi r^2 = \dfrac{50}{360} \times \pi \times 7.2^2$

$= 22.619...$

$= 22.6$ cm², correct to 3 s.f.

● Shapes formed by joining different shapes together are called **compound shapes**.
To find the area of a compound shape we must first divide the shape up into rectangles, triangles, circles, etc, and find the area of each part.

Exercise 25

Take π to be 3.14 or use the π key on your calculator.

1 A circular pond has a circumference of 12π metres.
Find an estimate, in terms of π, for the area of the pond.

2 Tranter has completed three-fifths of a circular jigsaw puzzle.
The puzzle has a radius of 20 cm.
What area of the puzzle is complete?

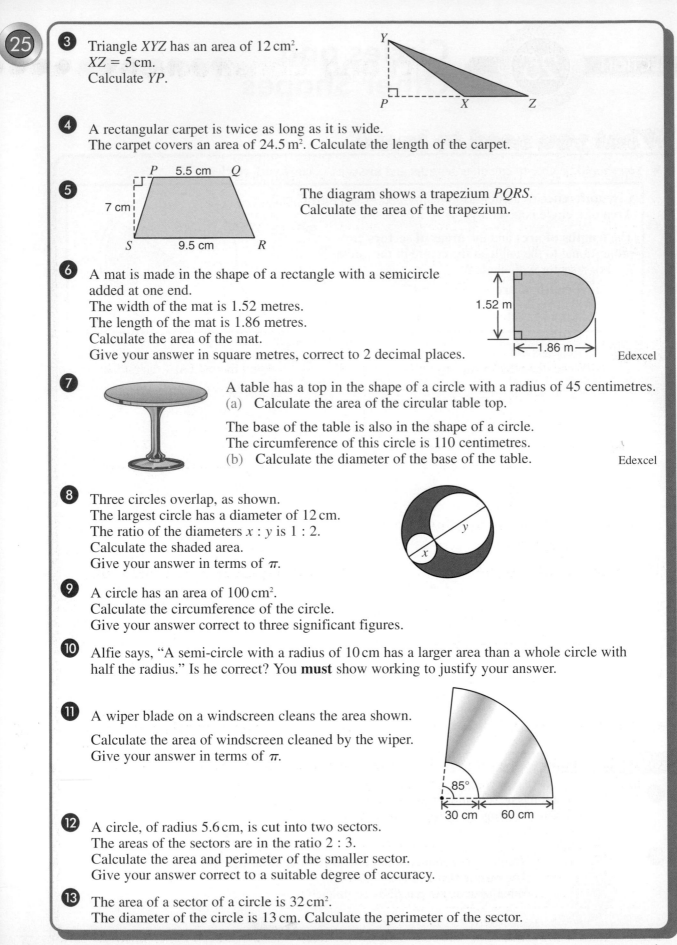

25

3 Triangle *XYZ* has an area of 12 cm².
XZ = 5 cm.
Calculate *YP*.

4 A rectangular carpet is twice as long as it is wide.
The carpet covers an area of 24.5 m². Calculate the length of the carpet.

5 The diagram shows a trapezium *PQRS*.
Calculate the area of the trapezium.

6 A mat is made in the shape of a rectangle with a semicircle
added at one end.
The width of the mat is 1.52 metres.
The length of the mat is 1.86 metres.
Calculate the area of the mat.
Give your answer in square metres, correct to 2 decimal places.

Edexcel

7 A table has a top in the shape of a circle with a radius of 45 centimetres.
(a) Calculate the area of the circular table top.

The base of the table is also in the shape of a circle.
The circumference of this circle is 110 centimetres.
(b) Calculate the diameter of the base of the table.

Edexcel

8 Three circles overlap, as shown.
The largest circle has a diameter of 12 cm.
The ratio of the diameters *x* : *y* is 1 : 2.
Calculate the shaded area.
Give your answer in terms of π.

9 A circle has an area of 100 cm².
Calculate the circumference of the circle.
Give your answer correct to three significant figures.

10 Alfie says, "A semi-circle with a radius of 10 cm has a larger area than a whole circle with
half the radius." Is he correct? You **must** show working to justify your answer.

11 A wiper blade on a windscreen cleans the area shown.

Calculate the area of windscreen cleaned by the wiper.
Give your answer in terms of π.

12 A circle, of radius 5.6 cm, is cut into two sectors.
The areas of the sectors are in the ratio 2 : 3.
Calculate the area and perimeter of the smaller sector.
Give your answer correct to a suitable degree of accuracy.

13 The area of a sector of a circle is 32 cm².
The diameter of the circle is 13 cm. Calculate the perimeter of the sector.

Loci and Constructions

What you need to know

- The path of a point which moves according to a rule is called a **locus**.

- The word **loci** is used when we talk about more than one locus.

- You should be able to draw the locus of a point which moves according to a given rule.

  Eg 1 A ball is rolled along this zig-zag. Draw the locus of *P*, the centre of the ball, as it is rolled along.

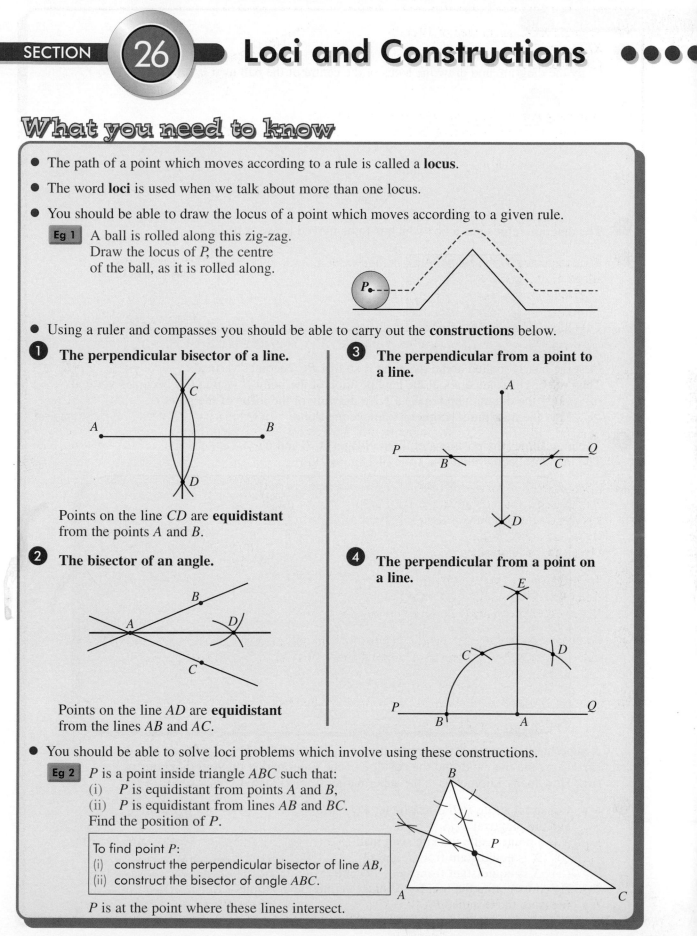

- Using a ruler and compasses you should be able to carry out the **constructions** below.

1 **The perpendicular bisector of a line.**

Points on the line *CD* are **equidistant** from the points *A* and *B*.

2 **The bisector of an angle.**

Points on the line *AD* are **equidistant** from the lines *AB* and *AC*.

3 **The perpendicular from a point to a line.**

4 **The perpendicular from a point on a line.**

- You should be able to solve loci problems which involve using these constructions.

  Eg 2 *P* is a point inside triangle *ABC* such that:
  (i)   *P* is equidistant from points *A* and *B*,
  (ii) *P* is equidistant from lines *AB* and *BC*.
  Find the position of *P*.

  To find point *P*:
  (i)   construct the perpendicular bisector of line *AB*,
  (ii) construct the bisector of angle *ABC*.

  P is at the point where these lines intersect.

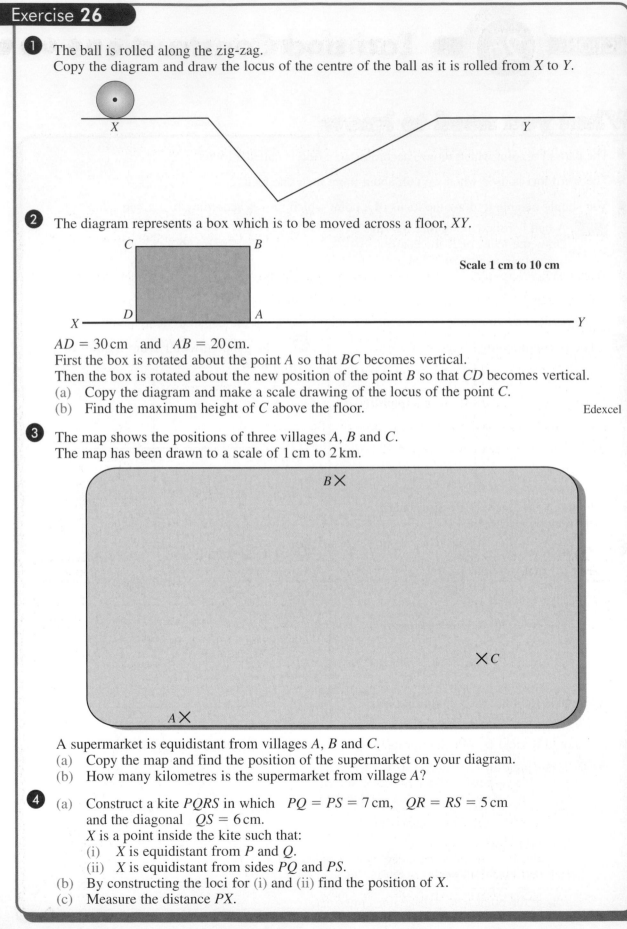

1 The ball is rolled along the zig-zag.
Copy the diagram and draw the locus of the centre of the ball as it is rolled from X to Y.

2 The diagram represents a box which is to be moved across a floor, XY.

Scale 1 cm to 10 cm

$AD = 30\,\text{cm}$ and $AB = 20\,\text{cm}$.
First the box is rotated about the point A so that BC becomes vertical.
Then the box is rotated about the new position of the point B so that CD becomes vertical.
(a) Copy the diagram and make a scale drawing of the locus of the point C.
(b) Find the maximum height of C above the floor. Edexcel

3 The map shows the positions of three villages A, B and C.
The map has been drawn to a scale of 1 cm to 2 km.

A supermarket is equidistant from villages A, B and C.
(a) Copy the map and find the position of the supermarket on your diagram.
(b) How many kilometres is the supermarket from village A?

4 (a) Construct a kite $PQRS$ in which $PQ = PS = 7\,\text{cm}$, $QR = RS = 5\,\text{cm}$
and the diagonal $QS = 6\,\text{cm}$.
X is a point inside the kite such that:
(i) X is equidistant from P and Q.
(ii) X is equidistant from sides PQ and PS.
(b) By constructing the loci for (i) and (ii) find the position of X.
(c) Measure the distance PX.

What you need to know

- The movement of a shape from one position to another is called a **transformation**.

- **Single transformations** can be described in terms of a reflection, a rotation, a translation or an enlargement.

- **Reflection**: The image of the shape is the same distance from the mirror line as the original.

- **Rotation**: All points are turned through the same angle about the same point, called a centre of rotation.

- **Translation**: All points are moved the same distance in the same direction without turning.

- **Enlargement**: All lengths are multiplied by a scale factor.

Scale factor $= \dfrac{\text{new length}}{\text{original length}}$ | New length = scale factor × original length |

The size of the original shape is:
  increased by using a scale factor greater than 1,
  reduced by using a scale factor which is a fraction, i.e. between 0 and 1.
When a shape is enlarged using a **negative scale factor** the image is **inverted**.

- You should be able to draw the transformation of a shape.

Eg 1 Draw the image of triangle P after it

has been translated with vector $\begin{pmatrix} -3 \\ 2 \end{pmatrix}$.

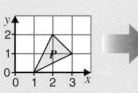

- You should be able to fully describe transformations.

Transformation	Image same shape and size?	Details needed to describe the transformation
Reflection	Yes	Mirror line, sometimes given as an equation.
Rotation	Yes	Centre of rotation, amount of turn, direction of turn.
Translation	Yes	Vector: top number = horizontal movement, bottom number = vertical movement.
Enlargement	No	Centre of enlargement, scale factor.

Eg 2 Describe the single transformation which maps
  (a) A onto B,
  (b) A onto C,
  (c) A onto D,
  (d) D onto E,
  (e) E onto F.

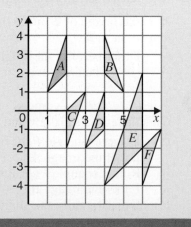

  (a) **reflection** in the line $x = 3$.
  (b) **rotation** of $180°$ about $(2, 1)$.

  (c) **translation** with vector $\begin{pmatrix} 2 \\ -3 \end{pmatrix}$.

  (d) **enlargement** scale factor 2, centre $(2, 0)$.

  (e) **enlargement** scale factor $-\frac{1}{2}$, centre $(6, -2)$.

1 The diagram shows the positions of kites *P*, *Q*, *R* and *S*.

(a) (i) *P* is mapped onto *Q* by a reflection.
What is the equation of the
line of reflection?

(ii) *P* is mapped onto *R* by a translation.
What is the vector of the translation?

(iii) *P* is mapped onto *S* by an enlargement.
What is the centre and scale factor of
the enlargement?

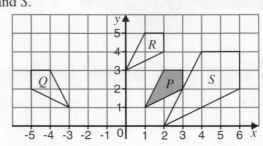

(b) *P* is mapped onto *T* by a rotation through 90° clockwise about $(1, -2)$.
On squared paper, copy *P* and draw the position of *T*.

2 In each diagram, *A* is mapped onto *B* by a single transformation. Describe each transformation.

(a)

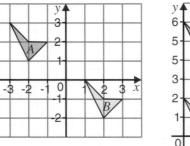

(b)

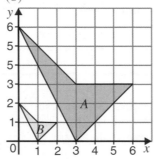

(c)

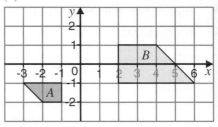

3 Triangle *X* has vertices $(1, 2)$, $(0, 3)$, $(-1, 1)$.
Triangle *Y* has vertices $(2, 1)$, $(3, 0)$, $(1, -1)$.
Describe the single transformation which maps *X* onto *Y*.

4 The diagram shows triangles *T*, *S* and *U*.
S is the image of *T* under a reflection in
the line $x = 3$.
U is the image of *S* under a reflection in
the line $x = 6$.

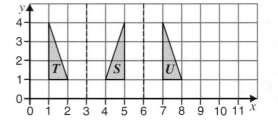

A reflection in the line $x = 3n$,
where *n* is an integer, is denoted by R_n.
So *S* is the image of *T* under R_1 and *U* is the image of *T* under R_1, followed by R_2.
V is the image of *T* under the successive transformations R_1, followed by R_2, followed by R_3.

(a) Copy the diagram and draw *V*.

(b) Describe fully the single transformation that will map *T* to *V*.

W is the image of *T* under the successive transformations R_1, followed by R_2, followed by R_3,
and so on to R_n.

(c) Describe fully the single transformation that will map *T* to *W*
(i) when *n* is even, (ii) when *n* is odd.

Edexcel

5 Triangle *PQR* has vertices $P(2, -3)$, $Q(-2, -5)$, $R(-4, -3)$.
On squared paper, draw and label triangle *PQR*.

(a) Enlarge triangle *PQR* by scale factor $\frac{1}{2}$ from the centre of enlargement $(4, -1)$.
Label the image *A*.

(b) Rotate triangle *PQR* through 180° about the point $(-2, -1)$.
Label the image *B*.

(c) Describe fully the single transformation which maps triangle *A* onto triangle *B*.

Pythagoras' Theorem

What you need to know

- The longest side in a right-angled triangle is called the **hypotenuse**.

- The **Theorem of Pythagoras** states:
  "In any right-angled triangle the square on the hypotenuse is equal to the sum of the squares on the other two sides."
  $$a^2 = b^2 + c^2$$

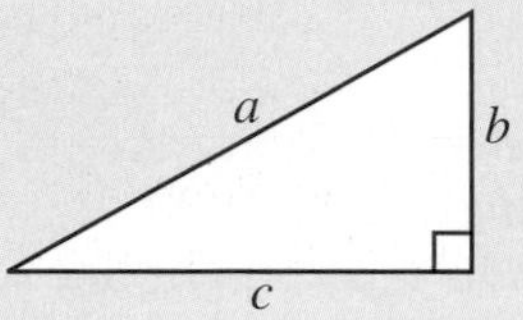

- When we know the lengths of two sides of a right-angled triangle, we can use the Theorem of Pythagoras to find the length of the third side.

$$a^2 = b^2 + c^2$$
Rearranging gives: $b^2 = a^2 - c^2$
$$c^2 = a^2 - b^2$$

Eg 1 Calculate the length of side a, correct to 1 d.p.

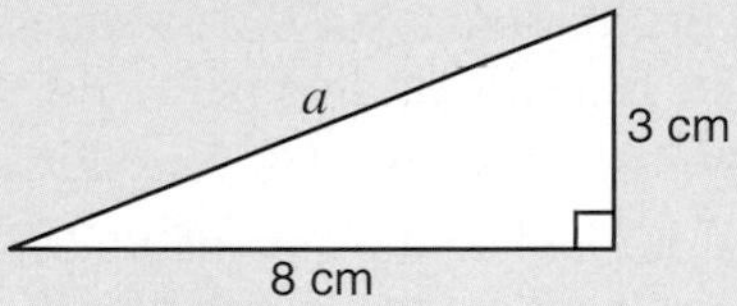

$a^2 = b^2 + c^2$
$a^2 = 8^2 + 3^2$
$a^2 = 64 + 9 = 73$
$a = \sqrt{73} = 8.544...$
$a = 8.5$ cm, correct to 1 d.p.

Eg 2 Calculate the length of side b, correct to 1 d.p.

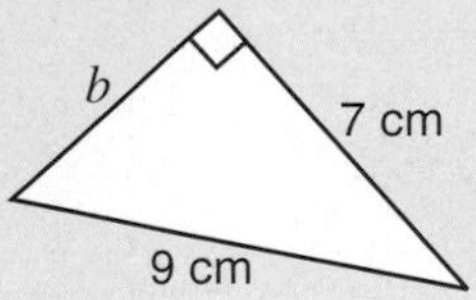

$b^2 = a^2 - c^2$
$b^2 = 9^2 - 7^2$
$b^2 = 81 - 49 = 32$
$b = \sqrt{32} = 5.656...$
$b = 5.7$ cm, correct to 1 d.p.

- When solving problems in three dimensions you often need to use more than one triangle to solve the problem.

Exercise 28

The diagrams in this exercise have not been drawn accurately.
Do not use a calculator for questions 1 and 2.

1 ABC is a right-angled triangle.
$AB = 5$ cm and $AC = 12$ cm.
Calculate the length of BC.

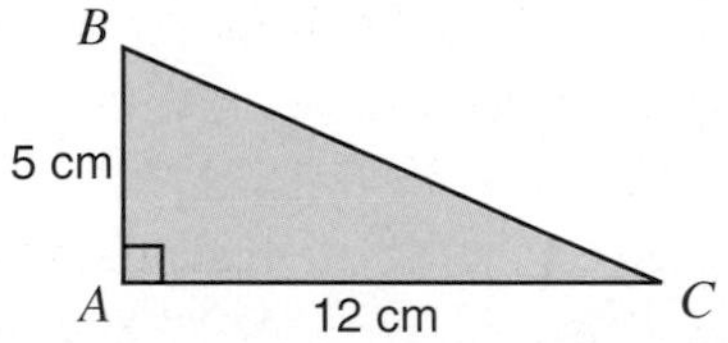

2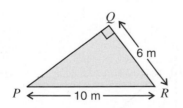

The diagram shows the cross-section of the roof of a house.
The width of the house, PR, is 10 m.
$QR = 6$ m and angle $PQR = 90°$.
Calculate the length of PQ.

3 The diagram shows a rectangular sheet of paper.
The paper is 20 cm wide and the diagonal, d, is 35 cm.
Calculate the length of the sheet of paper.

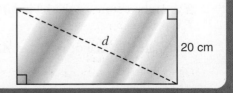

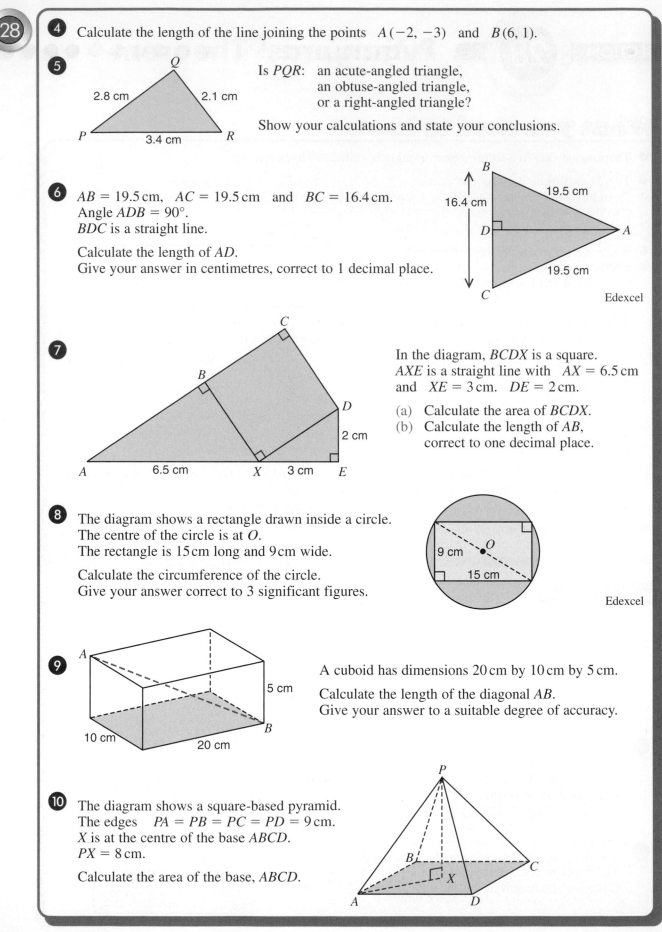

28

4 Calculate the length of the line joining the points $A(-2, -3)$ and $B(6, 1)$.

5

Q

2.8 cm   2.1 cm

P   3.4 cm   R

Is PQR: an acute-angled triangle,
            an obtuse-angled triangle,
            or a right-angled triangle?

Show your calculations and state your conclusions.

6 $AB = 19.5\,\text{cm}$, $AC = 19.5\,\text{cm}$ and $BC = 16.4\,\text{cm}$.
Angle $ADB = 90°$.
BDC is a straight line.

Calculate the length of AD.
Give your answer in centimetres, correct to 1 decimal place.

Edexcel

7

C

B

D

2 cm

A   6.5 cm   X   3 cm   E

In the diagram, $BCDX$ is a square.
AXE is a straight line with $AX = 6.5\,\text{cm}$
and $XE = 3\,\text{cm}$. $DE = 2\,\text{cm}$.

(a)   Calculate the area of $BCDX$.
(b)   Calculate the length of AB,
      correct to one decimal place.

8 The diagram shows a rectangle drawn inside a circle.
The centre of the circle is at O.
The rectangle is 15 cm long and 9 cm wide.

Calculate the circumference of the circle.
Give your answer correct to 3 significant figures.

Edexcel

9

A

5 cm

10 cm   20 cm   B

A cuboid has dimensions 20 cm by 10 cm by 5 cm.

Calculate the length of the diagonal AB.
Give your answer to a suitable degree of accuracy.

10 The diagram shows a square-based pyramid.
The edges $PA = PB = PC = PD = 9\,\text{cm}$.
X is at the centre of the base $ABCD$.
$PX = 8\,\text{cm}$.

Calculate the area of the base, $ABCD$.

What you need to know

- **Trigonometry** is used to find the lengths of sides and the sizes of angles in right-angled triangles.

- You must learn the **sine**, **cosine** and **tangent** ratios.

$$\sin a = \frac{\text{opposite}}{\text{hypotenuse}} \quad \cos a = \frac{\text{adjacent}}{\text{hypotenuse}} \quad \tan a = \frac{\text{opposite}}{\text{adjacent}}$$

hypotenuse

opposite

adjacent

a

- Each ratio links the size of an angle with the lengths of two sides. If we are given the values for two of these we can find the value of the third.

- When we look **up** from the horizontal the angle we turn through is called the **angle of elevation**.

- When we look **down** from the horizontal the angle we turn through is called the **angle of depression**.

Angle of elevation

horizontal

Angle of depression

- **Three-figure bearings**

  Bearings are used to describe the direction in which you must travel to get from one place to another. They are measured from the North line in a clockwise direction. A bearing can be any angle from 0° to 360° and is written as a three-figure number.

- You should be able to use trigonometry to find the lengths of sides and the sizes of angles when solving problems involving right-angled triangles.

Eg 1 Find the length, d, giving the answer to 3 significant figures.

62°

6.6 m (adj)

d (opp)

$$\tan a = \frac{\text{opp}}{\text{adj}}$$

$$\tan 62° = \frac{d}{6.6}$$

$$d = 6.6 \times \tan 62°$$

$$d = 12.412\ldots$$

$$d = 12.4 \, \text{m, correct to 3 s.f.}$$

Eg 2 Find the size of angle a, correct to one decimal place.

16 cm (hyp)

11 cm (opp)

a

$$\sin a = \frac{\text{opp}}{\text{hyp}}$$

$$\sin a° = \frac{11}{16}$$

$$a = \sin^{-1} \frac{11}{16}$$

$$a = 43.432\ldots$$

$$a = 43.4°, \text{correct to 1 d.p.}$$

- When working in three dimensions the first task is to identify the length, or angle, that you are trying to find. The length, or angle, will always form part of a triangle together with either:

  two other sides of known length, or

  one side of known length and an angle of known size.

  Sometimes, more than one triangle is needed to solve a problem.

- A straight line meets a plane at a **point**.

  The angle XPT is the **angle between the line and the plane**.

  The line XT is perpendicular to the plane.

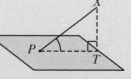

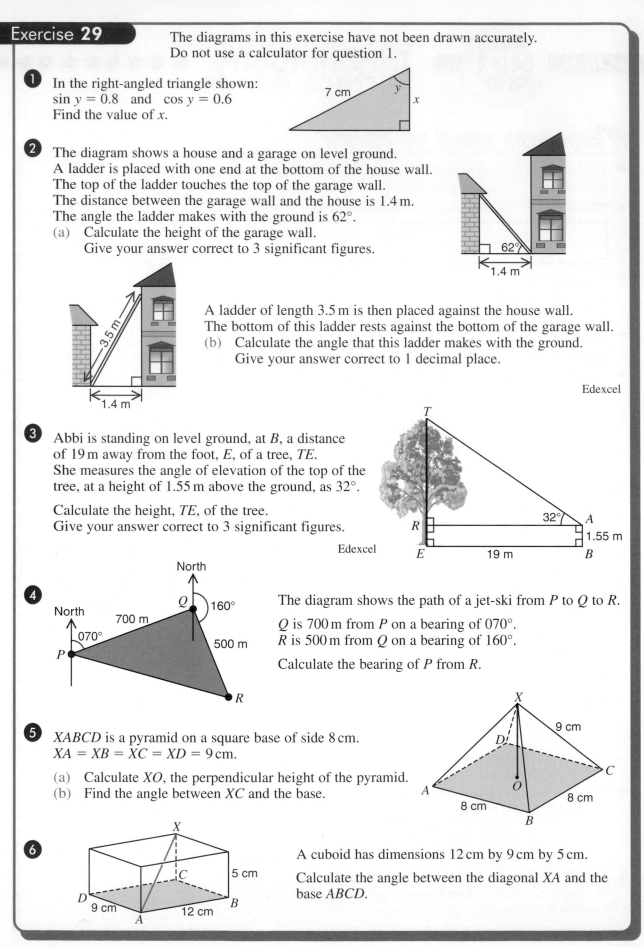

The diagrams in this exercise have not been drawn accurately.
Do not use a calculator for question 1.

1 In the right-angled triangle shown:
sin $y = 0.8$ and   cos $y = 0.6$
Find the value of x.

7 cm

y

x

2 The diagram shows a house and a garage on level ground.
A ladder is placed with one end at the bottom of the house wall.
The top of the ladder touches the top of the garage wall.
The distance between the garage wall and the house is 1.4 m.
The angle the ladder makes with the ground is 62°.
  (a) Calculate the height of the garage wall.
       Give your answer correct to 3 significant figures.

62°

1.4 m

3.5 m

1.4 m

A ladder of length 3.5 m is then placed against the house wall.
The bottom of this ladder rests against the bottom of the garage wall.
  (b) Calculate the angle that this ladder makes with the ground.
       Give your answer correct to 1 decimal place.

Edexcel

3 Abbi is standing on level ground, at B, a distance
of 19 m away from the foot, E, of a tree, TE.
She measures the angle of elevation of the top of the
tree, at a height of 1.55 m above the ground, as 32°.

Calculate the height, TE, of the tree.
Give your answer correct to 3 significant figures.

Edexcel

T

R 32° A

1.55 m

E 19 m B

4 North

North

Q 160°

700 m

070°

500 m

P

R

The diagram shows the path of a jet-ski from P to Q to R.

Q is 700 m from P on a bearing of 070°.
R is 500 m from Q on a bearing of 160°.

Calculate the bearing of P from R.

5 $XABCD$ is a pyramid on a square base of side 8 cm.
$XA = XB = XC = XD = 9$ cm.

  (a) Calculate XO, the perpendicular height of the pyramid.
  (b) Find the angle between XC and the base.

X

9 cm

D

C

A O

8 cm   8 cm

B

6 X

C 5 cm

D

9 cm B

A 12 cm

A cuboid has dimensions 12 cm by 9 cm by 5 cm.

Calculate the angle between the diagonal XA and the
base $ABCD$.

Volumes and Surface Areas

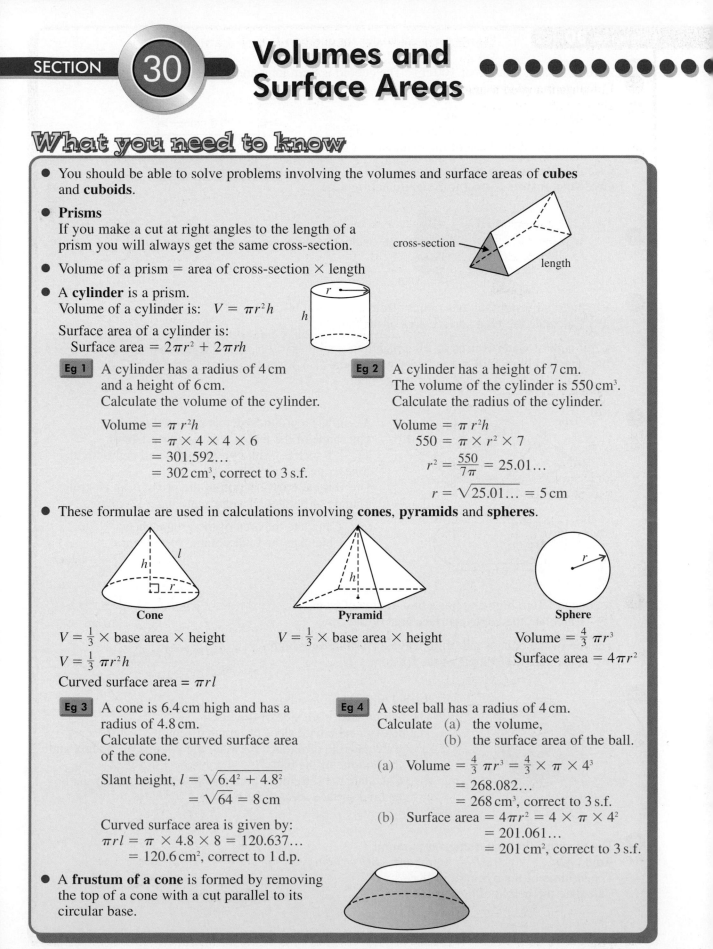

What you need to know

- You should be able to solve problems involving the volumes and surface areas of **cubes** and **cuboids**.

- **Prisms**
  If you make a cut at right angles to the length of a prism you will always get the same cross-section.

- Volume of a prism = area of cross-section × length

- A **cylinder** is a prism.
  Volume of a cylinder is: $V = \pi r^2 h$

  Surface area of a cylinder is:
  $$\text{Surface area} = 2\pi r^2 + 2\pi rh$$

  Eg 1 A cylinder has a radius of 4 cm and a height of 6 cm.
  Calculate the volume of the cylinder.

  $$\begin{aligned}
  \text{Volume} &= \pi\, r^2 h \\
  &= \pi \times 4 \times 4 \times 6 \\
  &= 301.592\ldots \\
  &= 302\ \text{cm}^3, \text{ correct to 3 s.f.}
  \end{aligned}$$

  Eg 2 A cylinder has a height of 7 cm.
  The volume of the cylinder is 550 cm³.
  Calculate the radius of the cylinder.

  $$\begin{aligned}
  \text{Volume} &= \pi\, r^2 h \\
  550 &= \pi \times r^2 \times 7 \\
  r^2 &= \frac{550}{7\pi} = 25.01\ldots \\
  r &= \sqrt{25.01\ldots} = 5\ \text{cm}
  \end{aligned}$$

- These formulae are used in calculations involving **cones**, **pyramids** and **spheres**.

  Cone
  $V = \frac{1}{3} \times \text{base area} \times \text{height}$
  $V = \frac{1}{3}\pi r^2 h$
  Curved surface area $= \pi r l$

  Pyramid
  $V = \frac{1}{3} \times \text{base area} \times \text{height}$

  Sphere
  Volume $= \frac{4}{3}\pi r^3$
  Surface area $= 4\pi r^2$

  Eg 3 A cone is 6.4 cm high and has a radius of 4.8 cm.
  Calculate the curved surface area of the cone.

  Slant height, $l = \sqrt{6.4^2 + 4.8^2}$
  $\qquad = \sqrt{64} = 8\ \text{cm}$

  Curved surface area is given by:
  $\pi r l = \pi \times 4.8 \times 8 = 120.637\ldots$
  $\qquad = 120.6\ \text{cm}^2$, correct to 1 d.p.

  Eg 4 A steel ball has a radius of 4 cm.
  Calculate (a) the volume,
  (b) the surface area of the ball.

  (a) Volume $= \frac{4}{3}\pi r^3 = \frac{4}{3} \times \pi \times 4^3$
  $\qquad = 268.082\ldots$
  $\qquad = 268\ \text{cm}^3$, correct to 3 s.f.

  (b) Surface area $= 4\pi r^2 = 4 \times \pi \times 4^2$
  $\qquad = 201.061\ldots$
  $\qquad = 201\ \text{cm}^2$, correct to 3 s.f.

- A **frustum of a cone** is formed by removing the top of a cone with a cut parallel to its circular base.

Do not use a calculator for question 1.

1 A cuboid has a volume of 100 cm³. The cuboid is 8 cm long and 5 cm wide.
Calculate the surface area of the cuboid.

2 The diagram shows a cylinder.
The height of the cylinder is 26.3 cm.
The diameter of the base of the cylinder is 8.6 cm.

Calculate the volume of the cylinder.
Give your answer correct to 3 significant figures.

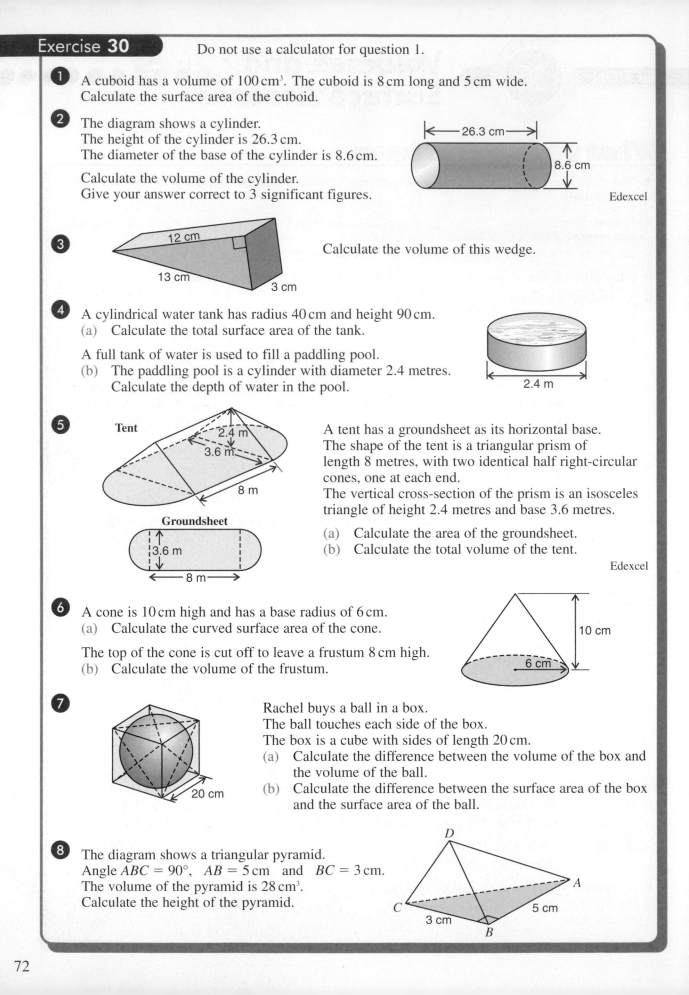

Edexcel

3 Calculate the volume of this wedge.

4 A cylindrical water tank has radius 40 cm and height 90 cm.
(a) Calculate the total surface area of the tank.

A full tank of water is used to fill a paddling pool.
(b) The paddling pool is a cylinder with diameter 2.4 metres.
Calculate the depth of water in the pool.

5 **Tent**

A tent has a groundsheet as its horizontal base.
The shape of the tent is a triangular prism of
length 8 metres, with two identical half right-circular
cones, one at each end.
The vertical cross-section of the prism is an isosceles
triangle of height 2.4 metres and base 3.6 metres.

(a) Calculate the area of the groundsheet.
(b) Calculate the total volume of the tent.

Edexcel

6 A cone is 10 cm high and has a base radius of 6 cm.
(a) Calculate the curved surface area of the cone.

The top of the cone is cut off to leave a frustum 8 cm high.
(b) Calculate the volume of the frustum.

7 Rachel buys a ball in a box.
The ball touches each side of the box.
The box is a cube with sides of length 20 cm.
(a) Calculate the difference between the volume of the box and
the volume of the ball.
(b) Calculate the difference between the surface area of the box
and the surface area of the ball.

8 The diagram shows a triangular pyramid.
Angle $ABC = 90°$, $AB = 5$ cm and $BC = 3$ cm.
The volume of the pyramid is 28 cm³.
Calculate the height of the pyramid.

Understanding and Using Measures

What you need to know

- The common units — both **metric** and **imperial** — used to measure **length**, **mass** and **capacity**.

- How to convert from one unit to another. This includes knowing the connection between one metric unit and another and the approximate equivalents between metric and imperial units.

Metric Units	Imperial Units	Conversions
Length 1 kilometre (km) = 1000 metres (m) 1 m = 100 centimetres (cm) 1 cm = 10 mm **Mass** 1 tonne (t) = 1000 kilograms (kg) 1 kg = 1000 grams (g) **Capacity and volume** 1 litre = 1000 millilitres (ml) $1 \, cm^3 = 1$ ml	**Length** 1 foot = 12 inches 1 yard = 3 feet **Mass** 1 pound = 16 ounces 14 pounds = 1 stone **Capacity and volume** 1 gallon = 8 pints	**Length** 5 miles is about 8 km 1 inch is about 2.5 cm 1 foot is about 30 cm **Mass** 1 kg is about 2.2 pounds **Capacity and volume** 1 litre is about 1.75 pints 1 gallon is about 4.5 litres

- How to change between units of area.   For example $1 \, m^2 = 10\,000 \, cm^2$.

- How to change between units of volume.   For example $1 \, m^3 = 1\,000\,000 \, cm^3$.

- A **discrete measure** can only take a particular value and a **continuous measure** lies within a range of possible values which depends upon the degree of accuracy of the measurement.

  Eg 1 A log is 12 m in length. The length is correct to the nearest metre.
  What is the minimum length of the log?   Minimum length = 12 − 0.5 = 11.5 m

  Eg 2 A road is 400 m long, to the nearest 10 m.
  Between what lengths is the actual length of the road?
  Actual length = 400 m ± 5 m   395 m ≤ actual length < 405 m

  Eg 3 Barry weighs a punnet of strawberries.
  He records the weight as 2.4 kg.
  The weight is recorded to the nearest tenth of a kilogram.
  What are the upper and lower bounds of the possible weights?

  Weight = 2.4 kg ± 0.05 kg

  Upper bound = 2.45 kg
  Lower bound = 2.35 kg

  > If a **continuous measure**, c, is recorded to the nearest x, then:
  > **Upper bound** $= c + \frac{1}{2}x$ **Lower bound** $= c - \frac{1}{2}x$

- By analysing the **dimensions** of a formula it is possible to decide whether a given formula represents a **length** (dimension 1), an **area** (dimension 2) or a **volume** (dimension 3).

  Eg 4 p, q, r and s represent lengths.
  By using dimensions, decide whether the expression $pq + qr + rs$
  could represent a perimeter, an area or a volume.
  Writing $pq + qr + rs$ using dimensions:
  $$L \times L + L \times L + L \times L = L^2 + L^2 + L^2 = 3L^2$$
  So, $pq + qr + rs$ has dimension 2 and could represent an area.

1 On a map the distance between two hospitals is 14.5 cm.
The map has been drawn to a scale of 1 to 250 000.
Calculate the actual distance between the hospitals in kilometres.

2 Mum's Traditional Jam is sold in two sizes.
A 1 lb pot of jam costs 71 pence. A 1 kg pot of jam costs £1.50.
Which pot of jam is better value for money? You must show all your working.

3 Debbie is 5 feet 4 inches tall and weighs 9 stone 2 lb. Joyce is 155 cm tall and weighs 60 kg.
Who is taller? Who is heavier? You must show your working.

4 Last year Felicity drove 2760 miles on business.
Her car does 38 miles per gallon. Petrol costs 69 pence per litre.
She is given a car allowance of 25 pence per kilometre.
How much of her car allowance is left after paying for her petrol?
Give your answer to the nearest £.

5 Jafar has a piece of wood that has a length of 30 cm, correct to the nearest centimetre.
(a) Write down the minimum length of the piece of wood.

Fatima has a different piece of wood that has a length of 18.4 cm,
correct to the nearest millimetre.
(b) Write down the maximum and minimum lengths between which the length of the
piece of wood must lie.
Edexcel

6 Some of the expressions shown in the table below can be used to calculate areas or volumes
of various shapes.
π and 2 are numbers which have no dimensions. The letters r, b and h represent lengths.

$2\pi r$	πr^2	$2bh$	πr^3	b^2h	$r^2 + b^3$

(a) Which of these expressions can be used to calculate an area?
(b) Which of these expressions can be used to calculate a volume?
Edexcel

7 Correct to 3 decimal places, $a = 2.236$.
(a) For this value of a, write down (i) the upper bound, (ii) the lower bound.

Correct to 3 decimal places, $b = 1.414$.
(b) Calculate (i) the upper bound for the value of $a + b$,
(ii) the lower bound for the value of $a + b$.
(c) Calculate the lower bound for the value of ab.
(d) Calculate the upper bound for the value of $\frac{a}{b}$.
Edexcel

8 The measurements of a rectangular ticket are given as 5 cm by 3 cm,
correct to the nearest centimetre.
(a) Between what limits must the width of the ticket lie?
(b) Between what limits must the area of the ticket lie?
(c) The area of the ticket is given as $(15 \pm x)\,\text{cm}^2$.
Suggest a suitable value for x.

9 Michael rides his bicycle to work.
The diameter of each wheel is 65 cm, correct to the nearest centimetre.
The distance he cycles to work is 2.4 km, correct to one decimal place.
Calculate the least number of turns each wheel makes when Michael cycles to work.

10 $x = 3$, correct to 1 significant figure.
$y = 0.06$, correct to 1 significant figure.
Calculate the greatest possible value of $y - \frac{x - 7}{x}$.
Edexcel

Congruent Triangles and Similar Figures

What you need to know

- When two shapes are the same shape and size they are said to be **congruent**.

- There are four ways to show that a pair of triangles are congruent.

SSS	3 corresponding sides.	**ASA**	2 angles and a corresponding side.
SAS	2 sides and the included angle.	**RHS**	Right angle, hypotenuse and one other side.

Eg 1 Show that triangles ABC and XYZ are congruent.

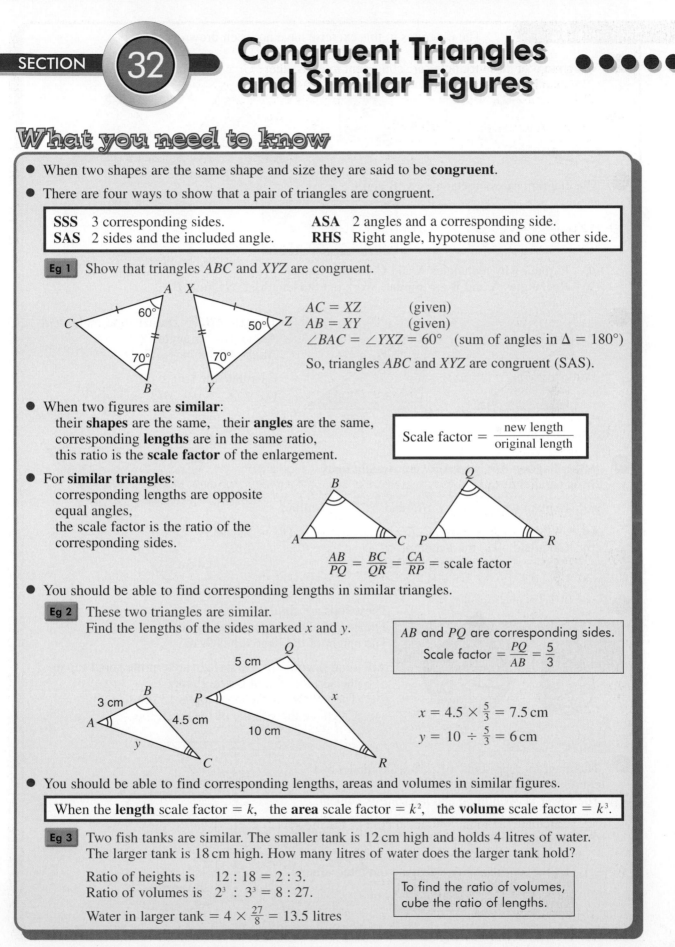

$AC = XZ$ (given)
$AB = XY$ (given)
$\angle BAC = \angle YXZ = 60°$ (sum of angles in $\Delta = 180°$)

So, triangles ABC and XYZ are congruent (SAS).

- When two figures are **similar**:
  their **shapes** are the same,   their **angles** are the same,
  corresponding **lengths** are in the same ratio,
  this ratio is the **scale factor** of the enlargement.

$$\text{Scale factor} = \frac{\text{new length}}{\text{original length}}$$

- For **similar triangles**:
  corresponding lengths are opposite
  equal angles,
  the scale factor is the ratio of the
  corresponding sides.

$$\frac{AB}{PQ} = \frac{BC}{QR} = \frac{CA}{RP} = \text{scale factor}$$

- You should be able to find corresponding lengths in similar triangles.

Eg 2 These two triangles are similar.
Find the lengths of the sides marked x and y.

AB and PQ are corresponding sides.
$$\text{Scale factor} = \frac{PQ}{AB} = \frac{5}{3}$$

$$x = 4.5 \times \tfrac{5}{3} = 7.5 \,\text{cm}$$
$$y = 10 \div \tfrac{5}{3} = 6 \,\text{cm}$$

- You should be able to find corresponding lengths, areas and volumes in similar figures.

When the **length** scale factor $= k$,   the **area** scale factor $= k^2$,   the **volume** scale factor $= k^3$.

Eg 3 Two fish tanks are similar. The smaller tank is 12 cm high and holds 4 litres of water.
The larger tank is 18 cm high. How many litres of water does the larger tank hold?

Ratio of heights is $12 : 18 = 2 : 3$.
Ratio of volumes is $2^3 : 3^3 = 8 : 27$.

To find the ratio of volumes,
cube the ratio of lengths.

Water in larger tank $= 4 \times \frac{27}{8} = 13.5$ litres

The diagrams in this exercise have not been drawn accurately.

1 Which two of these triangles are congruent to each other? Give a reason for your answer.

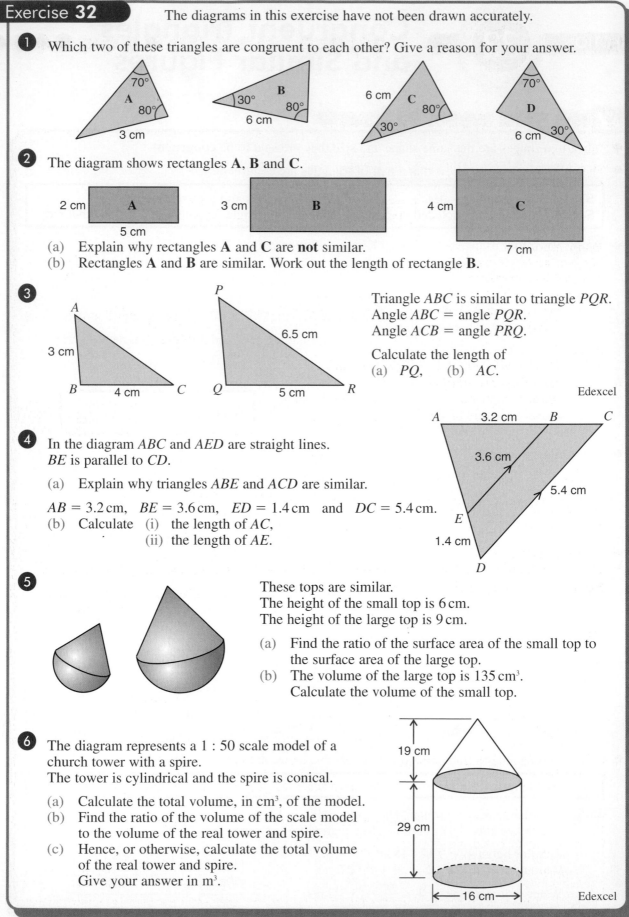

2 The diagram shows rectangles **A**, **B** and **C**.

2 cm **A**
5 cm

3 cm **B**

4 cm **C**
7 cm

(a) Explain why rectangles **A** and **C** are **not** similar.
(b) Rectangles **A** and **B** are similar. Work out the length of rectangle **B**.

3

A
3 cm
B 4 cm *C*

P
6.5 cm
Q 5 cm *R*

Triangle *ABC* is similar to triangle *PQR*.
Angle *ABC* = angle *PQR*.
Angle *ACB* = angle *PRQ*.

Calculate the length of
(a) *PQ*,   (b) *AC*.

Edexcel

4 In the diagram *ABC* and *AED* are straight lines.
BE is parallel to *CD*.

(a) Explain why triangles *ABE* and *ACD* are similar.

AB = 3.2 cm,   *BE* = 3.6 cm,   *ED* = 1.4 cm   and   *DC* = 5.4 cm.
(b) Calculate   (i)   the length of *AC*,
                (ii) the length of *AE*.

A 3.2 cm *B*   *C*
3.6 cm
5.4 cm
E
1.4 cm
D

5 These tops are similar.
The height of the small top is 6 cm.
The height of the large top is 9 cm.

(a) Find the ratio of the surface area of the small top to the surface area of the large top.
(b) The volume of the large top is 135 cm³.
    Calculate the volume of the small top.

6 The diagram represents a 1 : 50 scale model of a church tower with a spire.
The tower is cylindrical and the spire is conical.

(a) Calculate the total volume, in cm³, of the model.
(b) Find the ratio of the volume of the scale model to the volume of the real tower and spire.
(c) Hence, or otherwise, calculate the total volume of the real tower and spire.
    Give your answer in m³.

19 cm

29 cm

16 cm

Edexcel

What you need to know

- **Vector quantities**
  Quantities which have both **size** and **direction** are called **vectors**.
  Examples of vector quantities are:

  Displacement – A combination of distance and direction.

  Velocity – A combination of speed and direction.

- **Vector notation**
  Vectors can be represented by **column vectors** or by
  directed line segments.
  Vectors can be labelled using:
      capital letters to indicate the start and finish of a vector,
      bold lower case letters.

  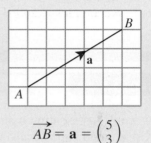

  $$\overrightarrow{AB} = \mathbf{a} = \begin{pmatrix} 5 \\ 3 \end{pmatrix}$$

  In a **column vector:**
      The top number describes the **horizontal**
      part of the movement:
      + = to the right   − = to the left

      The bottom number describes the **vertical**
      part of the movement:
      + = upwards   − = downwards

- Vectors are **equal** if they have the same length **and** they are in the same direction.
  Vectors $\mathbf{a}$ and $-\mathbf{a}$ have the same length **but** are in **opposite directions**.
  The vector $n\mathbf{a}$ is parallel to the vector $\mathbf{a}$.
  The length of vector $n\mathbf{a} = n \times$ the length of vector $\mathbf{a}$.

- **Vector addition**
  The combination of the displacement from A to B followed by the displacement from B to C is
  equivalent to a total displacement from A to C.

  This can be written using vectors as $\overrightarrow{AB} + \overrightarrow{BC} = \overrightarrow{AC}$

  $\overrightarrow{AC}$ is called the **resultant vector**.

- Combinations of vectors can be shown on **vector diagrams**.

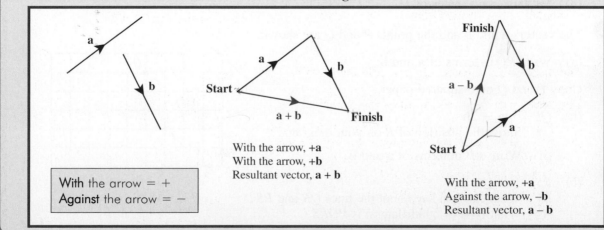

With the arrow = +
Against the arrow = −

With the arrow, +**a**
With the arrow, +**b**
Resultant vector, **a** + **b**

With the arrow, +**a**
Against the arrow, −**b**
Resultant vector, **a** − **b**

● You should be able to use **vector geometry** to solve simple geometrical problems, which can often involve parallel lines.

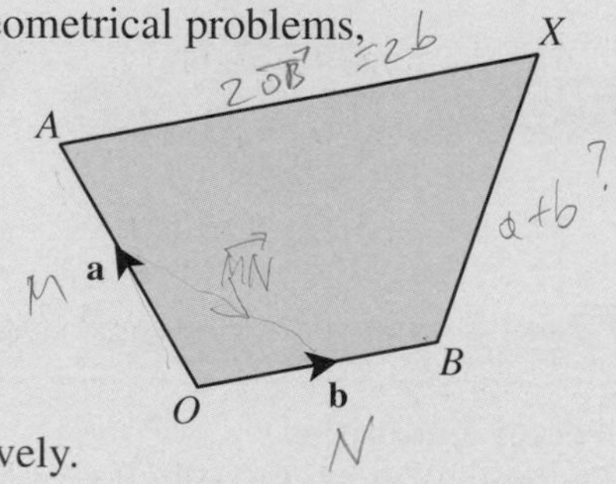

Eg 1 $OAXB$ is a quadrilateral.

$\overrightarrow{OA} = \mathbf{a}$, $\overrightarrow{OB} = \mathbf{b}$ and $\overrightarrow{AX} = 2\overrightarrow{OB}$.

(a) Find, in terms of $\mathbf{a}$ and $\mathbf{b}$,

   (i) $\overrightarrow{AX}$,   (ii) $\overrightarrow{BX}$.

(b) M and N are the midpoints of OA and BX respectively.

   (i) Find $\overrightarrow{MN}$, in terms of $\mathbf{a}$ and $\mathbf{b}$.
   (ii) What can you say about the lines OB and MN?
   (iii) What type of quadrilateral is $OMNB$?

(a) (i) $\overrightarrow{AX} = 2\mathbf{b}$ (ii) $\overrightarrow{BX} = \mathbf{a} + \mathbf{b}$

(b) (i) $\overrightarrow{MN} = 1\frac{1}{2}\mathbf{b}$ (ii) $2\overrightarrow{MN} = 3\overrightarrow{OB}$ (iii) Trapezium
                                       MN is parallel to OB.

Exercise 33   The diagrams in this exercise have not been drawn accurately.

1   Vectors representing $\mathbf{a}$ and $\mathbf{b}$ are drawn, as shown.
On squared paper, draw and label a vector to represent

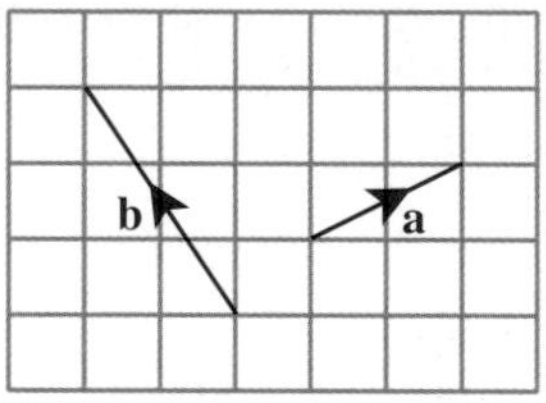

(a) $\mathbf{a} + \mathbf{b}$,

(b) $\mathbf{a} - \mathbf{b}$,

(c) $2\mathbf{a} + \mathbf{b}$.

2   In the diagram, $\overrightarrow{OX} = \mathbf{x}$ and $\overrightarrow{OY} = \mathbf{y}$.

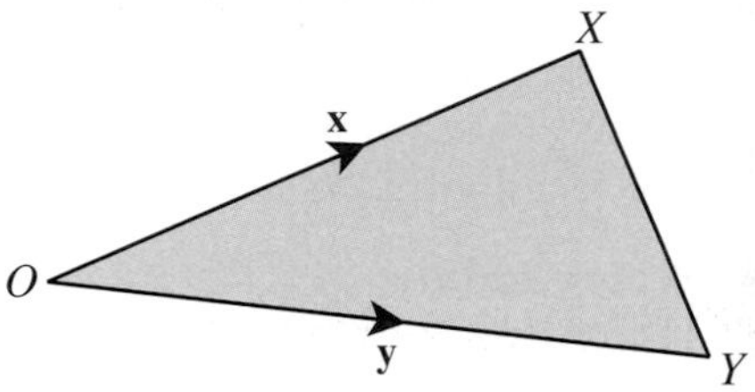

(a) Write, in terms of $\mathbf{x}$ and $\mathbf{y}$, the vector $\overrightarrow{XY}$.

(b) P and Q are the midpoints of OX and OY respectively.

    Find, in terms of $\mathbf{x}$ and $\mathbf{y}$, the vector $\overrightarrow{QP}$.

3 A is the point $(-3, 5)$ and B is the point $(3, 1)$.

(a) Find $\overrightarrow{AB}$ as a column vector.

C and D are points such that $\overrightarrow{CB} = \begin{pmatrix} -2 \\ -3 \end{pmatrix}$, and $ABCD$ is a trapezium with $\overrightarrow{AB} = 2\overrightarrow{DC}$.
(b) Find the coordinates of D.

4   The vectors $\mathbf{a}$ and $\mathbf{b}$ and the points P and Q are shown.

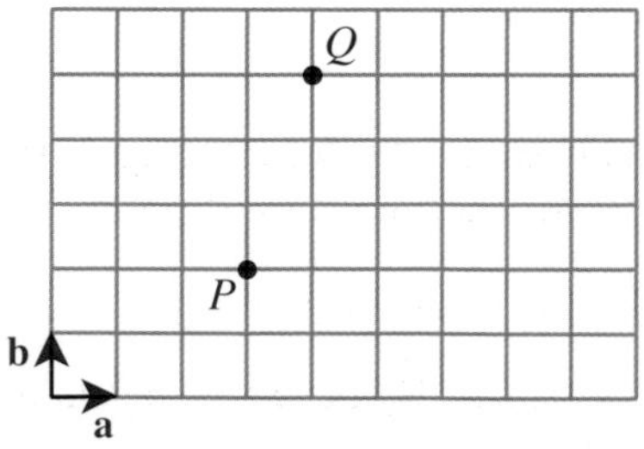

(a) Write $\overrightarrow{PQ}$ in terms of $\mathbf{a}$ and $\mathbf{b}$.

Copy P and Q onto squared paper.

(b) $\overrightarrow{QR} = 4\mathbf{a} - 2\mathbf{b}$.
   (i) Show the position of R on your diagram.
   (ii) Write $\overrightarrow{RP}$ in terms of $\mathbf{a}$ and $\mathbf{b}$.

(c) $\overrightarrow{RS} = -\overrightarrow{PQ}$
   (i) What can you say about the lines QR and PS?
   (ii) What type of quadrilateral is $PQRS$?

5 *A* is the point (2, 3) and *B* is the point (−2, 0).

    (a) (i)   Write $\overrightarrow{AB}$ as a column vector.

         (ii) Find the length of the vector $\overrightarrow{AB}$.

D is the point such that $\overrightarrow{BD}$ is parallel to $\begin{pmatrix} 0 \\ 1 \end{pmatrix}$ and the length of $\overrightarrow{AD}$ = the length of $\overrightarrow{AB}$. *O* is the point (0, 0).

    (b) Find $\overrightarrow{OD}$ as a column vector.

C is the point such that *ABCD* is a rhombus. *AC* is a diagonal of the rhombus.

    (c) Find the coordinates of *C*.

Edexcel

6 *PQRS* is a parallelogram.
T is the midpoint of *QR*.
U is the point on *SR* for which *SU* : *UR* = 1 : 2.
$\overrightarrow{PQ} = \mathbf{a}$ and $\overrightarrow{PS} = \mathbf{b}$.

Write down, in terms of **a** and **b**, expressions for

    (a) $\overrightarrow{PT}$,   (b) $\overrightarrow{TU}$.

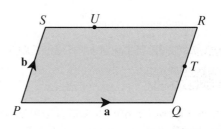

Edexcel

7 *ABC* is a triangle.
P and *Q* are the midpoints of *AB* and *AC* respectively.
Show that *PQ* is parallel to *BC* and is half its length.

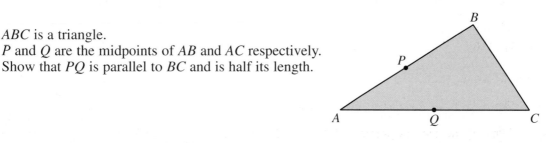

8 *A* is the point (1, 3) and *B* is the point (−3, 0).

    (a) Find $\overrightarrow{AB}$ as a column vector.

C is the point such that $\overrightarrow{BC} = \begin{pmatrix} 4 \\ 9 \end{pmatrix}$.

    (b) Write down the coordinates of the point *C*.

X is the midpoint of *AB*. *O* is the origin.

    (c) Find $\overrightarrow{OX}$ as a column vector.

Edexcel

9 The diagram shows a triangle *ABC*.
P is the midpoint of *AB* and *Q* is the point on *AC* such that   *QC* = 2*AQ*.
$\overrightarrow{AP} = \mathbf{x}$ and $\overrightarrow{AQ} = \mathbf{y}$.

    (a) Write $\overrightarrow{PQ}$ in terms of **x** and **y**.

T is a point such that $\overrightarrow{AT} = \overrightarrow{BC}$.

    (b) Show that *PQT* is a straight line.

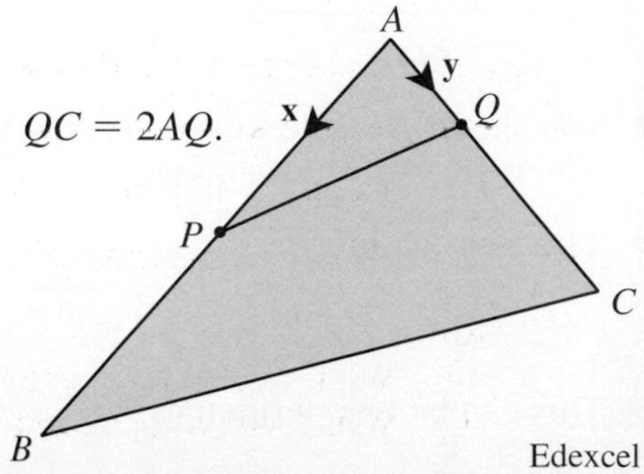

Edexcel

Vectors . . . Vectors . . . . Vectors . . . Vectors . . .

Further Trigonometry

What you need to know

- The graphs of the trigonometric functions.

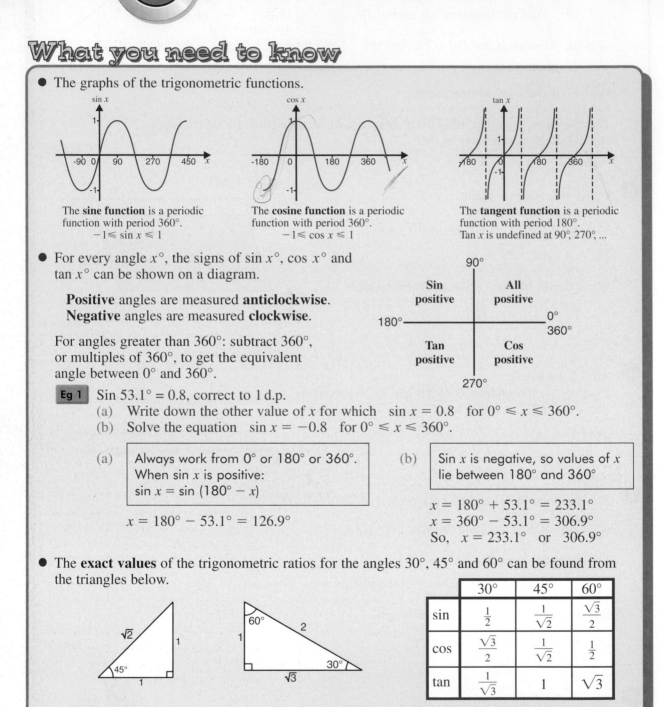

The **sine function** is a periodic function with period 360°.
$$-1 \leqslant \sin x \leqslant 1$$

The **cosine function** is a periodic function with period 360°.
$$-1 \leqslant \cos x \leqslant 1$$

The **tangent function** is a periodic function with period 180°.
Tan x is undefined at 90°, 270°, ...

- For every angle $x°$, the signs of $\sin x°$, $\cos x°$ and $\tan x°$ can be shown on a diagram.

    Positive angles are measured **anticlockwise**.
    Negative angles are measured **clockwise**.

    For angles greater than 360°: subtract 360°, or multiples of 360°, to get the equivalent angle between 0° and 360°.

Sin positive	**All** positive
Tan positive	**Cos** positive

90° — Sin positive / All positive — 180° — Tan positive / Cos positive — 270°, 0° / 360°

Eg 1 Sin 53.1° = 0.8, correct to 1 d.p.
   (a) Write down the other value of x for which $\sin x = 0.8$ for $0° \leqslant x \leqslant 360°$.
   (b) Solve the equation $\sin x = -0.8$ for $0° \leqslant x \leqslant 360°$.

(a)
> Always work from 0° or 180° or 360°.
> When $\sin x$ is positive:
> $\sin x = \sin (180° - x)$

$x = 180° - 53.1° = 126.9°$

(b)
> Sin x is negative, so values of x lie between 180° and 360°

$x = 180° + 53.1° = 233.1°$
$x = 360° - 53.1° = 306.9°$
So, $x = 233.1°$ or $306.9°$

- The **exact values** of the trigonometric ratios for the angles 30°, 45° and 60° can be found from the triangles below.

	30°	45°	60°
sin	$\frac{1}{2}$	$\frac{1}{\sqrt{2}}$	$\frac{\sqrt{3}}{2}$
cos	$\frac{\sqrt{3}}{2}$	$\frac{1}{\sqrt{2}}$	$\frac{1}{2}$
tan	$\frac{1}{\sqrt{3}}$	1	$\sqrt{3}$

- You should be able to use the **sine rule** and the **cosine rule** to solve problems involving triangles which are not right-angled.

- **The Sine Rule**

$$\frac{a}{\sin A} = \frac{b}{\sin B} = \frac{c}{\sin C}$$

This can be also written as: $\dfrac{\sin A}{a} = \dfrac{\sin B}{b} = \dfrac{\sin C}{c}$

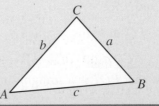

Eg 2 Calculate the length of side a, correct to 1 d.p.

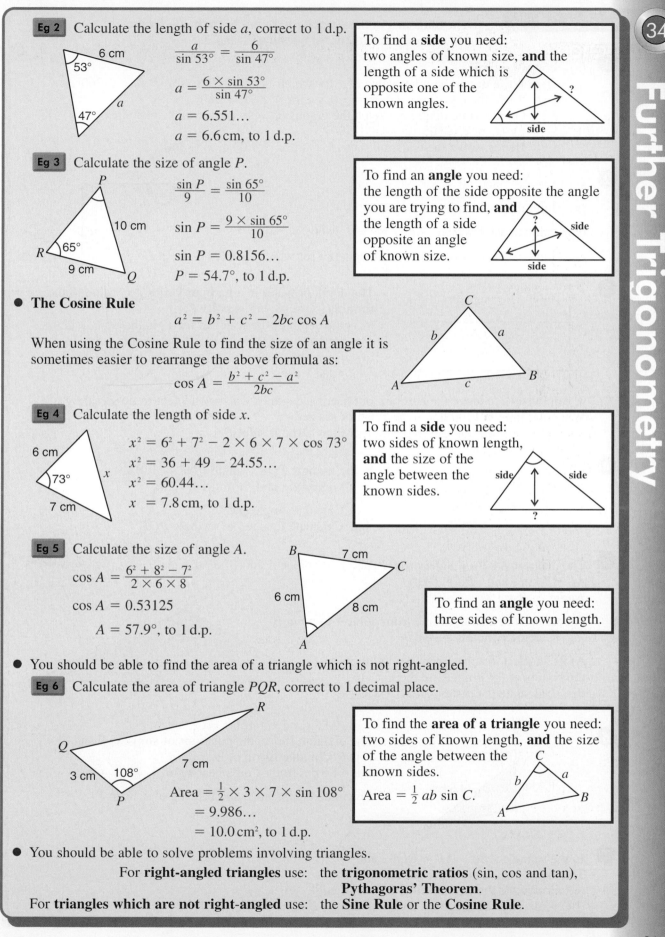

$$\frac{a}{\sin 53°} = \frac{6}{\sin 47°}$$

$$a = \frac{6 \times \sin 53°}{\sin 47°}$$

$$a = 6.551\ldots$$

$$a = 6.6\,\text{cm, to 1 d.p.}$$

To find a **side** you need:
two angles of known size, **and** the length of a side which is opposite one of the known angles.

Eg 3 Calculate the size of angle P.

$$\frac{\sin P}{9} = \frac{\sin 65°}{10}$$

$$\sin P = \frac{9 \times \sin 65°}{10}$$

$$\sin P = 0.8156\ldots$$

$$P = 54.7°\text{, to 1 d.p.}$$

To find an **angle** you need:
the length of the side opposite the angle you are trying to find, **and** the length of a side opposite an angle of known size.

- **The Cosine Rule**

$$a^2 = b^2 + c^2 - 2bc \cos A$$

When using the Cosine Rule to find the size of an angle it is sometimes easier to rearrange the above formula as:

$$\cos A = \frac{b^2 + c^2 - a^2}{2bc}$$

Eg 4 Calculate the length of side x.

$$x^2 = 6^2 + 7^2 - 2 \times 6 \times 7 \times \cos 73°$$

$$x^2 = 36 + 49 - 24.55\ldots$$

$$x^2 = 60.44\ldots$$

$$x = 7.8\,\text{cm, to 1 d.p.}$$

To find a **side** you need:
two sides of known length, **and** the size of the angle between the known sides.

Eg 5 Calculate the size of angle A.

$$\cos A = \frac{6^2 + 8^2 - 7^2}{2 \times 6 \times 8}$$

$$\cos A = 0.53125$$

$$A = 57.9°\text{, to 1 d.p.}$$

To find an **angle** you need:
three sides of known length.

- You should be able to find the area of a triangle which is not right-angled.

Eg 6 Calculate the area of triangle PQR, correct to 1 decimal place.

$$\text{Area} = \tfrac{1}{2} \times 3 \times 7 \times \sin 108°$$

$$= 9.986\ldots$$

$$= 10.0\,\text{cm}^2\text{, to 1 d.p.}$$

To find the **area of a triangle** you need:
two sides of known length, **and** the size of the angle between the known sides.

$$\text{Area} = \tfrac{1}{2}\,ab \sin C.$$

- You should be able to solve problems involving triangles.

For **right-angled triangles** use: the **trigonometric ratios** (sin, cos and tan), **Pythagoras' Theorem**.

For **triangles which are not right-angled** use: the **Sine Rule** or the **Cosine Rule**.

The diagrams in this exercise have not been drawn accurately.
Do not use a calculator for questions 1 and 2.

1 (a) $\cos 60° = 0.5$
    (i)   Write down the other value of x for which $\cos x = 0.5$ for $0° \leqslant x \leqslant 360°$.
    (ii)   Solve the equation $\cos x = -0.5$ for $0° \leqslant x \leqslant 360°$.
  (b)   (i)   On the same diagram, sketch the graphs of $y = \cos x$ and $y = \sin x$
      for $0° \leqslant x \leqslant 360°$.
    (ii)   Hence, solve the equation $\cos x = \sin x$ for $0° \leqslant x \leqslant 360°$.

2 $\sin x° = \dfrac{\sqrt{3}}{2}$ and $0 < x < 90$.

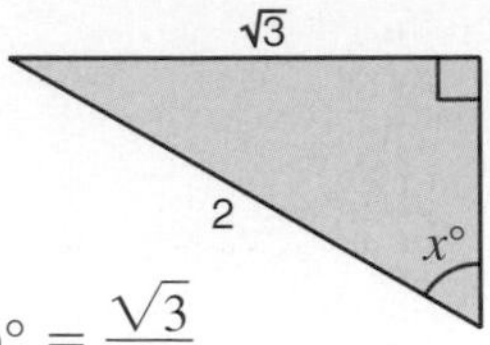

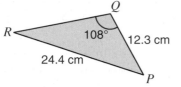

  (a)   Find the exact value of $\cos x°$.

One value of x for which $\sin x° = \dfrac{\sqrt{3}}{2}$ is 60.

  (b)   Find two values of y between 0 and 180 for which $\sin (2y)° = \dfrac{\sqrt{3}}{2}$.
                                                            Edexcel

3

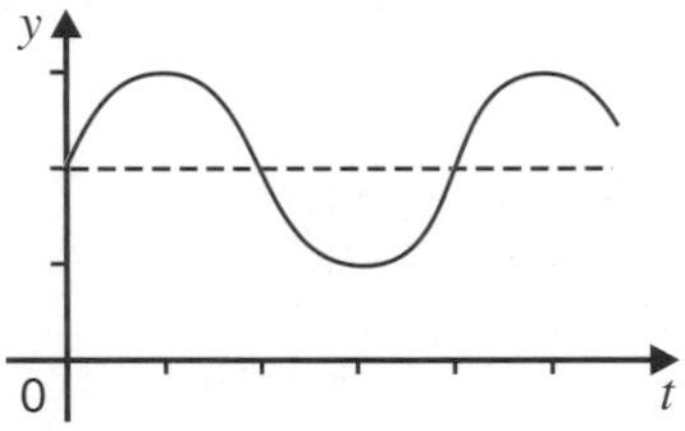

The depth of water in a harbour varies according to the
formula $y = 10 + 5 \sin (30t)°$.
(y is the depth of the water in feet; t is the time in hours.)
The sketch shows the graph of this formula.
  (a)   Copy the graph and complete the labelling on the
      t and y axes.

A ship wishes to leave the harbour, but needs a depth of water of 13 feet to do so safely.
When the time is 1200 hours the value of t is zero.
  (b)   At what time can the ship first leave the harbour safely?   Edexcel

4

In the triangle PQR,   angle $PQR = 108°$.
$PQ = 12.3\,\text{cm}$ and $PR = 24.4\,\text{cm}$.

  (a)   Calculate angle QRP.
  (b)   Calculate the area of triangle PQR.

5   The diagram shows a lighthouse, L, and two points, A and B, on the sea.
$AL = 5\,\text{km}$ and $BL = 6\,\text{km}$.
Angle $ALB = 150°$.

A boat sails in a straight line from point A to point B.
  (a)   Calculate the distance AB.

At its shortest distance from the lighthouse,
the boat is at the point X on the line AB.
  (b)   Calculate the distance LX.   Edexcel

6

The diagram shows the positions of ships X, Y and Z.
X is 6.3 km due North of Z.
Y is 14.5 km from X on a bearing of 127°.

Calculate the distance and bearing of Z from Y.

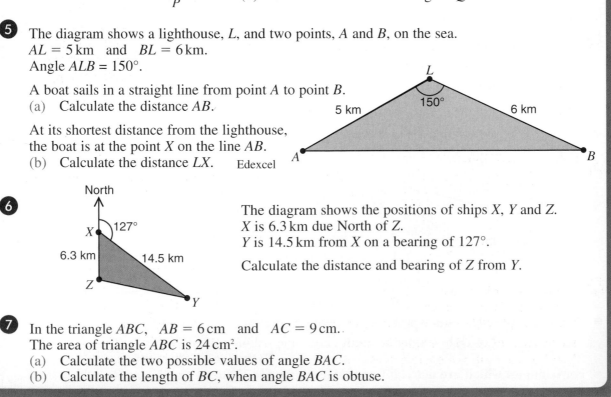

7   In the triangle ABC, $AB = 6\,\text{cm}$ and $AC = 9\,\text{cm}$.
The area of triangle ABC is $24\,\text{cm}^2$.
  (a)   Calculate the two possible values of angle BAC.
  (b)   Calculate the length of BC, when angle BAC is obtuse.

Section Review - Shape, Space and Measures

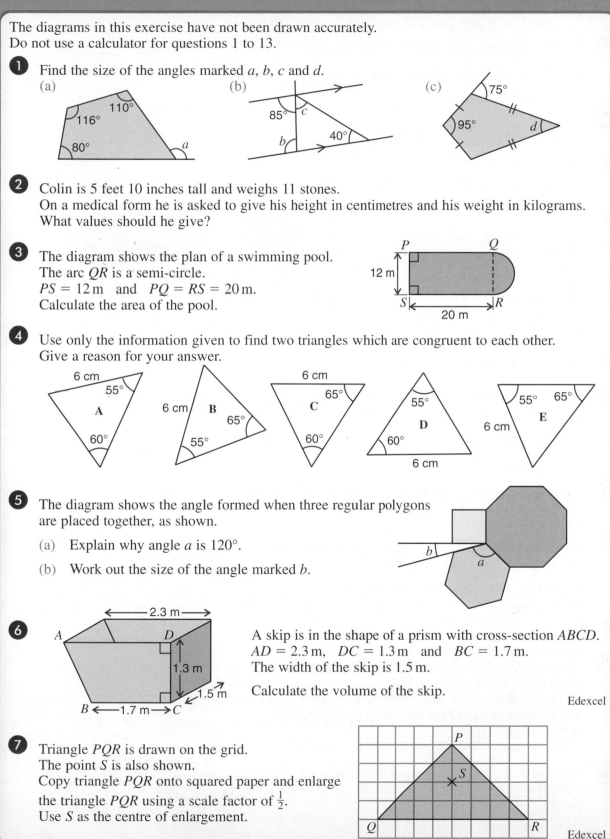

The diagrams in this exercise have not been drawn accurately.
Do not use a calculator for questions 1 to 13.

1 Find the size of the angles marked *a*, *b*, *c* and *d*.

(a)

110°
116°
80°
a

(b)

85°
c
b
40°

(c)

75°
95°
d

2 Colin is 5 feet 10 inches tall and weighs 11 stones.
On a medical form he is asked to give his height in centimetres and his weight in kilograms.
What values should he give?

3 The diagram shows the plan of a swimming pool.
The arc *QR* is a semi-circle.
PS = 12 m   and   *PQ* = *RS* = 20 m.
Calculate the area of the pool.

P   *Q*
12 m
S   *R*
20 m

4 Use only the information given to find two triangles which are congruent to each other.
Give a reason for your answer.

6 cm
55°
A
60°

6 cm
B
65°
55°

6 cm
65°
C
60°

55°
D
60°
6 cm

55° 65°
E
6 cm

5 The diagram shows the angle formed when three regular polygons are placed together, as shown.

(a)   Explain why angle *a* is 120°.

(b)   Work out the size of the angle marked *b*.

b
a

6

2.3 m
A   *D*
1.3 m
1.5 m
B ←1.7 m→ *C*

A skip is in the shape of a prism with cross-section *ABCD*.
AD = 2.3 m,   *DC* = 1.3 m   and   *BC* = 1.7 m.
The width of the skip is 1.5 m.

Calculate the volume of the skip.

Edexcel

7 Triangle *PQR* is drawn on the grid.
The point *S* is also shown.
Copy triangle *PQR* onto squared paper and enlarge
the triangle *PQR* using a scale factor of $\frac{1}{2}$.
Use *S* as the centre of enlargement.

P
S
Q   *R*

Edexcel

83

8 (a) Construct triangle ABC, in which $AB = 9.5\,cm$, $BC = 8\,cm$ and $CA = 6\,cm$.
(b) Using ruler and compasses only,
    (i) bisect angle BAC,   (ii) draw the locus of points that are equidistant from A and C.
(c) Shade the region inside the triangle where all the points are less than 7.5 cm from B, nearer to A than to C and nearer to AC than to AB.

9 (a) Calculate the sum of the interior angles of a regular 10-sided polygon.
(b) The diagram shows a square and a regular hexagon which meet at M.
LM and MN are two sides of another regular polygon.
How many sides has this polygon?

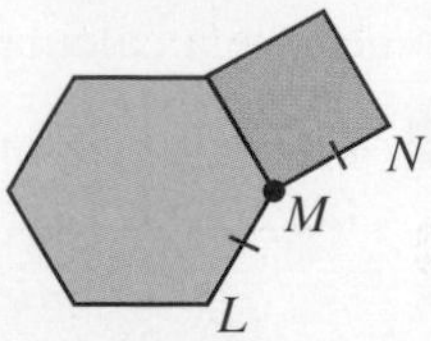

10 A circle has an area of $49\,\pi\,cm^2$.
Calculate the circumference of the circle, in terms of π.

11 Simone made a scale model of a "hot rod" car on a scale of 1 to 12.5.
The height of the model car is 10 cm.
(a) Work out the height of the real car.

The length of the real car is 5 m.
(b) Work out the length of the model car.
Give your answer in centimetres.

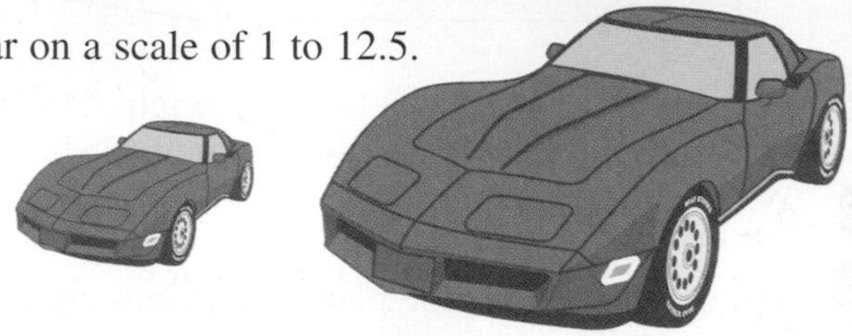

The angle the windscreen makes with the bonnet on the real car is 140°.
(c) What is the angle the windscreen makes with the bonnet on the model car?

The width of the windscreen in the real car is 119 cm, correct to the nearest centimetre.
(d) Write down the smallest length this measurement could be.
Edexcel

12 Tan $XYZ = \frac{4}{3}$.

(a) Find (i) sin XYZ,   (ii) cos XYZ.

(b) When $XZ = 10\,cm$, what are the lengths of XY and YZ?

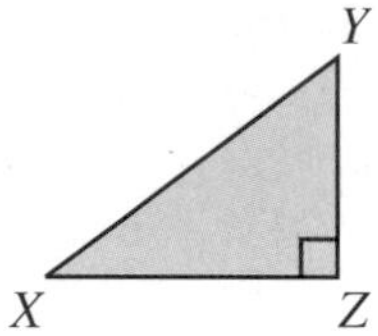

13 In these diagrams O is the centre of the circle.
Find the size of the angles a, b, c and x. Give a reason for each of your answers.
(a)   (b)   (c)

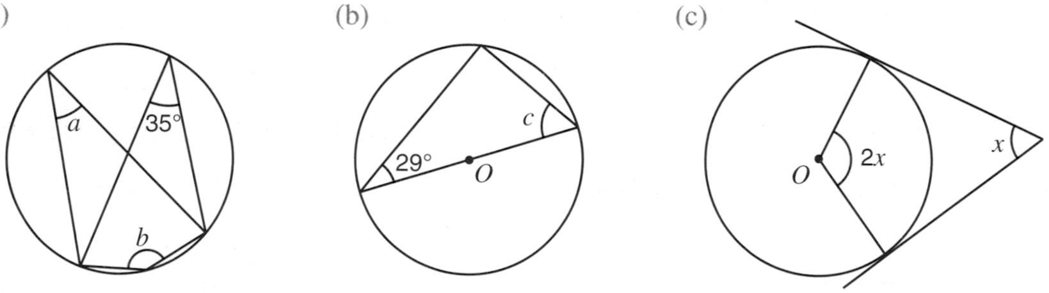

14 The diagram shows Fay's house, H, and her school, S.
To get to school Fay has a choice of two routes.
She can either walk along Waverly Crescent or along the footpaths HX and XS.
Waverly Crescent is a semi-circle with diameter 650 m.
The footpath HX is 250 m and meets the footpath XS at right-angles.
Which of these routes is shorter? By how much?

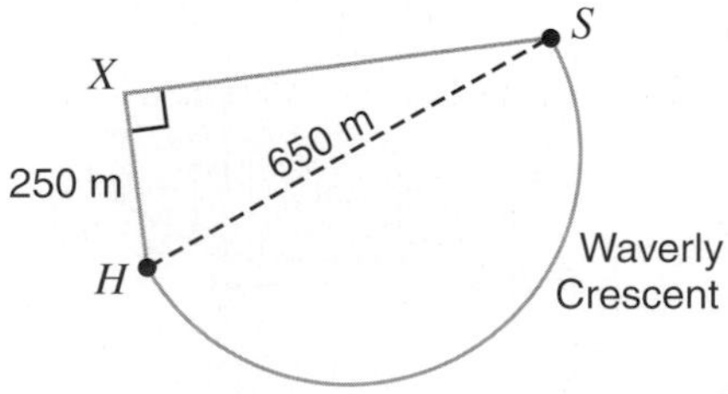

15 A cylindrical can has a radius of 6 centimetres.
The capacity of the can is $2000\,cm^3$.

Calculate the height of the can.
Give your answer correct to 1 decimal place. 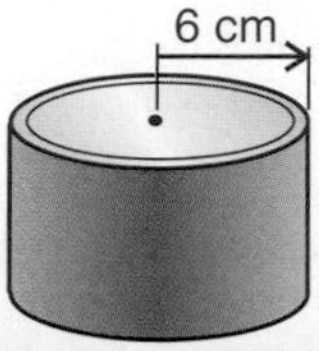
Edexcel

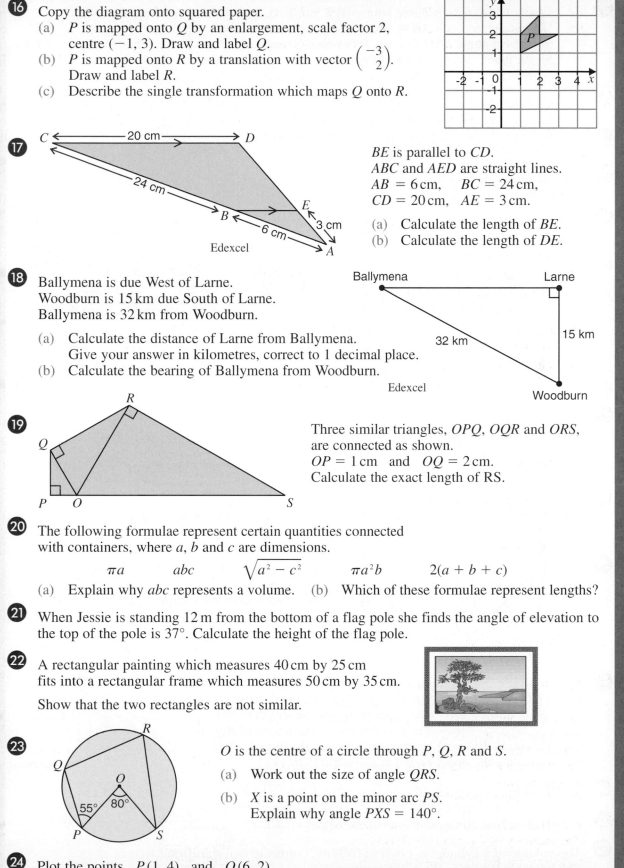

16 Copy the diagram onto squared paper.
   (a) P is mapped onto Q by an enlargement, scale factor 2, centre $(-1, 3)$. Draw and label Q.
   (b) P is mapped onto R by a translation with vector $\begin{pmatrix} -3 \\ 2 \end{pmatrix}$. Draw and label R.
   (c) Describe the single transformation which maps Q onto R.

17

C ←———— 20 cm ————→ D

24 cm

B ← 6 cm E 3 cm
A

Edexcel

BE is parallel to *CD*.
ABC and *AED* are straight lines.
$AB = 6$ cm, $BC = 24$ cm,
$CD = 20$ cm, $AE = 3$ cm.

   (a) Calculate the length of *BE*.
   (b) Calculate the length of *DE*.

18 Ballymena is due West of Larne.
Woodburn is 15 km due South of Larne.
Ballymena is 32 km from Woodburn.

   (a) Calculate the distance of Larne from Ballymena.
       Give your answer in kilometres, correct to 1 decimal place.
   (b) Calculate the bearing of Ballymena from Woodburn.

Edexcel

Ballymena ———————— Larne

32 km   15 km

Woodburn

19

R

Q

P O   S

Three similar triangles, *OPQ*, *OQR* and *ORS*, are connected as shown.
$OP = 1$ cm and $OQ = 2$ cm.
Calculate the exact length of RS.

20 The following formulae represent certain quantities connected with containers, where a, b and c are dimensions.

$$\pi a \qquad abc \qquad \sqrt{a^2 - c^2} \qquad \pi a^2 b \qquad 2(a + b + c)$$

   (a) Explain why abc represents a volume.   (b) Which of these formulae represent lengths?

21 When Jessie is standing 12 m from the bottom of a flag pole she finds the angle of elevation to the top of the pole is $37°$. Calculate the height of the flag pole.

22 A rectangular painting which measures 40 cm by 25 cm fits into a rectangular frame which measures 50 cm by 35 cm.

Show that the two rectangles are not similar.

23

R
Q
O
55° 80°
P S

O is the centre of a circle through P, Q, R and S.

   (a) Work out the size of angle *QRS*.

   (b) X is a point on the minor arc *PS*.
       Explain why angle $PXS = 140°$.

24 Plot the points $P(1, 4)$ and $Q(6, 2)$.
Construct accurately the locus of all points which are equidistant from P and Q.   Edexcel

Section Review . . . . Section Review . . . . Section Review

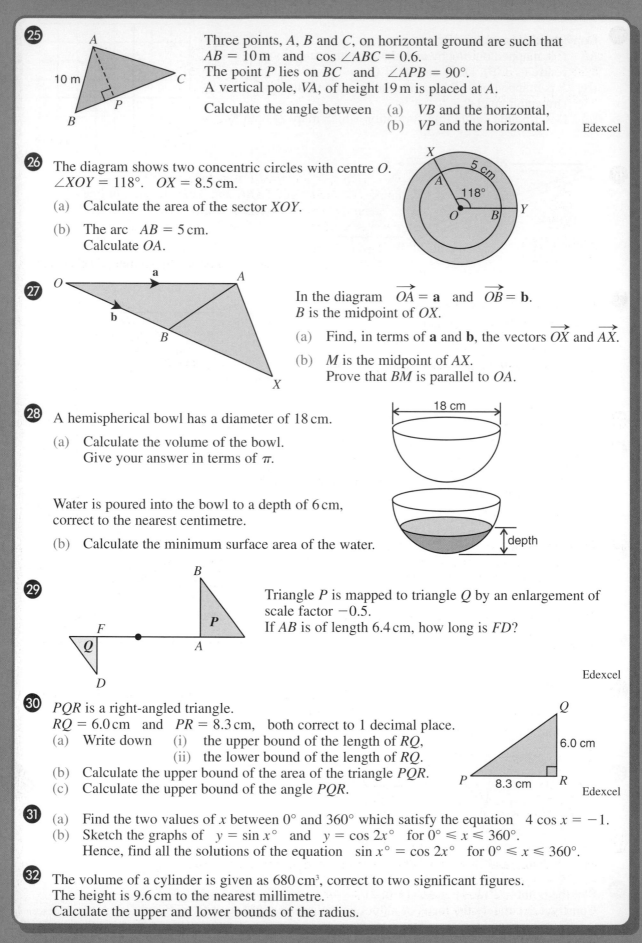

25

Three points, A, B and C, on horizontal ground are such that $AB = 10\,\text{m}$ and $\cos \angle ABC = 0.6$.
The point P lies on BC and $\angle APB = 90°$.
A vertical pole, VA, of height $19\,\text{m}$ is placed at A.

Calculate the angle between
(a) VB and the horizontal,
(b) VP and the horizontal.

Edexcel

26

The diagram shows two concentric circles with centre O.
$\angle XOY = 118°$. $OX = 8.5\,\text{cm}$.

(a) Calculate the area of the sector XOY.

(b) The arc $AB = 5\,\text{cm}$.
Calculate OA.

27

In the diagram $\overrightarrow{OA} = \mathbf{a}$ and $\overrightarrow{OB} = \mathbf{b}$.
B is the midpoint of OX.

(a) Find, in terms of $\mathbf{a}$ and $\mathbf{b}$, the vectors $\overrightarrow{OX}$ and $\overrightarrow{AX}$.

(b) M is the midpoint of AX.
Prove that BM is parallel to OA.

28

A hemispherical bowl has a diameter of $18\,\text{cm}$.

(a) Calculate the volume of the bowl.
Give your answer in terms of π.

Water is poured into the bowl to a depth of $6\,\text{cm}$, correct to the nearest centimetre.

(b) Calculate the minimum surface area of the water.

29

Triangle P is mapped to triangle Q by an enlargement of scale factor -0.5.
If AB is of length $6.4\,\text{cm}$, how long is FD?

Edexcel

30

PQR is a right-angled triangle.
$RQ = 6.0\,\text{cm}$ and $PR = 8.3\,\text{cm}$, both correct to 1 decimal place.
(a) Write down (i) the upper bound of the length of RQ,
(ii) the lower bound of the length of RQ.
(b) Calculate the upper bound of the area of the triangle PQR.
(c) Calculate the upper bound of the angle PQR.

Edexcel

31

(a) Find the two values of x between $0°$ and $360°$ which satisfy the equation $4 \cos x = -1$.
(b) Sketch the graphs of $y = \sin x°$ and $y = \cos 2x°$ for $0° \leqslant x \leqslant 360°$.
Hence, find all the solutions of the equation $\sin x° = \cos 2x°$ for $0° \leqslant x \leqslant 360°$.

32

The volume of a cylinder is given as $680\,\text{cm}^3$, correct to two significant figures.
The height is $9.6\,\text{cm}$ to the nearest millimetre.
Calculate the upper and lower bounds of the radius.

33 In the quadrilateral $ABCD$,
$AB = 6\,cm$, $BC = 7\,cm$, $AD = 12\,cm$,
angle $ABC = 120°$, angle $ACD = 70°$.

Calculate the size of angle ADC.

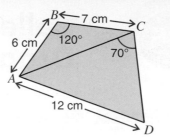

Edexcel

34  The stand on which the dog is sitting is the frustum of a cone.
The top of the stand has a radius of $0.5\,m$.
The bottom of the stand has a radius of $1\,m$.
The height of the stand is $0.6\,m$.

    (a) Calculate the volume of the stand.
    (b) The height of a similar stand is $0.4\,m$. Calculate the volume of this stand.

35 The diagram shows a triangular piece of card.
Angle BAC is obtuse, $AB = 5.8\,cm$ and $AC = 7.4\,cm$.
The area of the card is $20\,cm^2$.
Calculate the length of BC.
Give your answer to a suitable degree of accuracy.

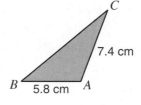

36
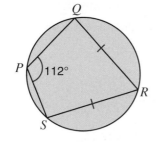
$PQRS$ is a cyclic quadrilateral in which:
$QR = RS$, $PS = 5.2\,cm$ and $PQ = 6.8\,cm$.
$\angle SPQ = 112°$.

Calculate the length of QR.

37 The diagram shows two triangles, OAB and OCD.
OAC and OBD are straight lines.
AB is parallel to CD.
$\overrightarrow{OA} = \mathbf{a}$ and $\overrightarrow{OB} = \mathbf{b}$.
The point A cuts the line OC in the ratio $OA : OC = 2 : 3$.

Express $\overrightarrow{CD}$ in terms of $\mathbf{a}$ and $\mathbf{b}$.
Edexcel

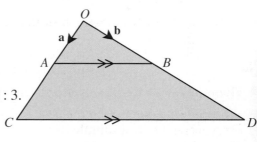

38
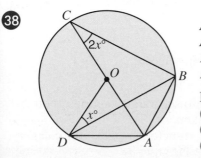
A, B, C, and D are points on the circumference of a circle centre O.
AC is a diameter of the circle.
Angle $BDO = x°$.
Angle $BCA = 2x°$.

Express, in terms of x, the size of
    (a) angle BDA,
    (b) angle AOD,
    (c) angle ABD.
Edexcel

39 George constructs a triangle, PQR.
$PQ = 8.5\,cm$ and $QR = 5.1\,cm$, correct to the nearest millimetre.
$\angle PQR = 118°$, correct to the nearest degree.
    (a) Calculate the upper bound of the side PR.
    (b) Calculate the lower bound for the area of triangle PQR.

Collection and Organisation of Data

What you need to know

- **Primary data** is data collected by an individual or organisation to use for a particular purpose. Primary data is obtained from experiments, investigations, surveys and by using questionnaires.

- **Secondary data** is data which is already available or has been collected by someone else for a different purpose. Sources of secondary data include the Annual Abstract of Statistics, Social Trends and the Internet.

- **Qualitative** data – Data which can only be described in words.

- **Quantitative** data – Data that has a numerical value. Quantitative data is either **discrete** or **continuous**. **Discrete** data can only take certain values. **Continuous** data has no exact value and is measurable.

- **Data Collection Sheets** – Used to record data during a survey.

- **Tally** – A way of recording each item of data on a data collection sheet.
  A group of five is recorded as ⊬⊬⊤.

- **Frequency Table** – A way of collating the information recorded on a data collection sheet.

- **Grouped Frequency Table** – Used for continuous data or for discrete data when a lot of data has to be recorded.

- **Database** – A collection of data.

- **Class Interval** – The width of the groups used in a grouped frequency distribution.

- **Questionnaire** – A set of questions used to collect data for a survey.
  Questionnaires should: (1) use simple language,
                          (2) ask short questions which can be answered precisely,
                          (3) provide tick boxes,
                          (4) avoid open-ended questions,
                          (5) avoid leading questions,
                          (6) ask questions in a logical order.

- **Hypothesis** – A hypothesis is a statement which may or may not be true.

- When information is required about a large group of people it is not always possible to survey everyone and only a **sample** may be asked.
  The sample chosen should be large enough to make the results meaningful and representative of the whole group (population) or the results may be **biased**.

- **Two-way Tables** – A way of illustrating two features of a survey.

- In a **simple random sample** everyone has an equal chance of being selected.

- In a **systematic random sample** people are selected according to some rule.

- In a **stratified random sample** the original group is divided up into separate categories or strata, such as male/female, age group, etc, before a random sample is taken.
  A simple random sample is then taken from each category in proportion to the size of the category.

Exercise 35

1 To find out how long students spend on homework each night, Pat asks a class of Year 7 students how much time they spent on their homework last night.
Give two reasons why his results may not be typical of all students.

Collection and Organisation of Data

2 Jamie is investigating the use made of his college library. Here is part of his questionnaire:

> **Library Questionnaire**
> 1. How old are you? ....

(a) (i) Give a reason why this question is unsuitable.
   (ii) Rewrite the question so that it could be included.

(b) Jamie asks the librarian to give the questionnaires to students when they borrow books.
   (i) Give reasons why this sample may be biased.
   (ii) Suggest a better way of giving out the questionnaires.

3 Martin, the local Youth Centre leader, wishes to know why attendance at the Youth Centre is less than at the same time last year.

He thinks that it could be due to a number of changes that occurred during the course of the year.

These changes were: the opening hours changed,
a new sports centre opened nearby,
some of the older members started bullying the younger members.

Design a suitable question, that is easily answered, to find out why people do not attend the Youth Centre.

Edexcel

4 The table shows the results of a survey of 500 people.

A newspaper headline states:

Survey shows that more women can drive than men.

	Can drive	Cannot drive
Men	180	20
Women	240	60

Do the results of the survey support this headline? Give a reason for your answer.

5 Explain briefly in what circumstances a stratified random sample might be taken rather than a simple random sample.

6 There are 1000 students in Nigel and Sonia's school.
Nigel is carrying out a survey of the types of food eaten at lunchtime.

(a) Explain how Nigel could take a random sample of students to carry out this survey.

This table shows the gender and the number of students in each year group.

Year group	Number of boys	Number of girls	Total
7	100	100	200
8	90	80	170
9	120	110	230
10	80	120	200
11	100	100	200

Sonia is carrying out a survey about how much homework students are given.
She decides to take a stratified sample of 100 students from the whole school.

(b) Calculate how many in the stratified sample should be
   (i) students from Year 9, (ii) boys from Year 10.

Edexcel

7 There are three secondary schools in a large town.
The number of pupils in each school is given in the table.

Albert High School	570
St Joseph's High School	965
London Road School	1015

A researcher wishes to find out what secondary school pupils feel about the standard of education in the town.
She chooses a representative sample of total size 50.
How many pupils should be chosen from each school?

Edexcel

Averages and Range ●●●●●

What you need to know

● There are three types of **average**: the **mode**, the **median** and the **mean**.

Eg 1 The number of text messages received by 7 students on Saturday is shown.

$$2 \quad 4 \quad 3 \quad 4 \quad 4 \quad 3 \quad 2$$

Find   (a) the mode,   (b) the median,   (c) the mean,   (d) the range.

> The **mode** is the most common amount.
>
> The **median** is found by arranging the data in order of size and taking the middle amount (or the mean of the two middle amounts).
>
> The **mean** is found by dividing the total of all the data by the number of data values.
>
> The **range** is a measure of **spread**.
> Range = highest amount − lowest amount

(a) The mode is 4.

(b) 2   2   3   ③   4   4   4
The median is 3.

(c) The mean $= \dfrac{2+4+3+4+4+3+2}{7}$

$\qquad\qquad = \dfrac{22}{7} = 3.14\ldots$

$\qquad\qquad = 3.1$, correct to 1 d.p.

(d) The range $= 4 - 2 = 2$

● To find the mean of a **frequency distribution** use:

$$\text{Mean} = \frac{\text{Total of all amounts}}{\text{Number of amounts}} = \frac{\Sigma fx}{\Sigma f}$$

Eg 2 The table shows the number of stamps on some parcels.

Number of stamps	1	2	3	4
Number of parcels	5	6	9	4

Find the mean number of stamps per parcel.

$\text{Mean} = \dfrac{\Sigma fx}{\Sigma f}$

$\qquad = \dfrac{1 \times 5 + 2 \times 6 + 3 \times 9 + 4 \times 4}{5 + 6 + 9 + 4}$

$\qquad = \dfrac{60}{24} = 2.5$

● To find the mean of a **grouped frequency distribution**, first find the value of the midpoint of each class.

Then use:

$$\text{Estimated mean} = \frac{\Sigma\,(\text{frequency} \times \text{midpoint})}{\text{Total frequency}} = \frac{\Sigma fx}{\Sigma f}$$

Eg 3 The table shows the weights of some parcels.

Weight (w grams)	Frequency
$100 \leqslant w < 200$	7
$200 \leqslant w < 300$	11
$300 \leqslant w < 400$	19
$400 \leqslant w < 500$	3

Calculate an estimate of the mean weight of these parcels.

$\text{Mean} = \dfrac{\Sigma fx}{\Sigma f}$

$\qquad = \dfrac{150 \times 7 + 250 \times 11 + 350 \times 19 + 450 \times 3}{7 + 11 + 19 + 3}$

$\qquad = \dfrac{11\,800}{40} = 295$ grams

● Choosing the best average to use:
   When the most **popular** value is wanted use the **mode**.
   When **half** of the values have to be above the average use the **median**.
   When a **typical** value is wanted use either the **mode** or the **median**.
   When all the **actual** values have to be taken into account use the **mean**.
   When the average should not be distorted by a few very small or very large values do **not** use the mean.

Do not use a calculator for questions 1 and 2.

1 The prices paid for eight different meals at a restaurant are:

£10   £9   £9.50   £12   £20   £11.50   £11   £9

(a) Which price is the mode?   (b) Find the median price.   (c) Calculate the mean price.

(d) Which of these averages best describes the average price paid for a meal?
Give a reason for your answer.

2 Some students took a mental arithmetic test.
Information about their marks is shown in the table.

(a) Work out how many students took the test.
(b) Write down the modal mark.

24 students had a higher mark than Caroline.
(c) Work out Caroline's mark.
(d) Find the median mark.
(e) Work out the range of the marks.

Mark	Frequency
4	2
5	1
6	2
7	4
8	7
9	10
10	3

Edexcel

3 75 boys took part in a darts competition.
Each boy threw darts until he hit the centre of the dartboard.
The numbers of darts thrown by the boys are grouped in this frequency table.

Number of darts thrown	Frequency
1 to 5	10
6 to 10	17
11 to 15	12
16 to 20	4
21 to 25	12
26 to 30	20

(a) Work out the class interval which contains the median.
(b) Work out an estimate for the mean number of darts thrown by each boy.   Edexcel

4 The table shows the number of students in three groups attending Maths City High School
last Monday. No student belonged to more than one group.

Group	A	B	C
Number of students	135	225	200

Mrs Allen carried out a survey about the students' travelling times from home to school
last Monday. Mrs Allen worked out that:

● the mean time for Group A students was 24 minutes,
● the mean time for Group B students was 32 minutes,
● the mean time for Group C students was the same as the mean time for all 560 students.

Work out the mean time for all 560 students.   Edexcel

5 A survey was carried out to find out how much time was needed by a group of pupils to
complete homework set on a particular Monday evening.
The results are shown in the table.

Time (t hours) spent on homework	0	$0 < t \leq 1$	$1 < t \leq 2$	$2 < t \leq 3$	$3 < t \leq 4$
Number of pupils	3	14	17	5	1

Calculate an estimate for the mean time spent on homework by the pupils in the group.   Edexcel

Presentation of Data 1

What you need to know

- **Bar chart**. Used for data which can be counted.
  Often used to compare quantities of data in a distribution.
  The length of each bar represents frequency.

  > Bars can be drawn horizontally or vertically.

- **Bar-line graph**. Instead of drawing bars, horizontal or vertical lines are drawn to show frequency.

- **Pie chart**. Used for data which can be counted.
  Often used to compare proportions of data, usually with the total.
  The whole circle represents all the data.
  The size of each sector represents the frequency of data in that sector.

- **Stem and leaf diagrams**. Used to represent data in its original form. Data is split into two parts.
  The part with the higher place value is the stem.   e.g.   15 = stem 1, leaf 5.
  A key is given to show the value of the data.   e.g.   3|4 means 3.4 etc.
  The data is shown in numerical order on the diagram.   e.g.   2|3 5 9 represents 23, 25, 29.
  Back to back stem and leaf diagrams can be used to compare two sets of data.

- A **scatter graph** can be used to show the relationship between two sets of data.

- The relationship between two sets of data is referred to as **correlation**.

- You should be able to recognise **positive** and **negative** correlation.

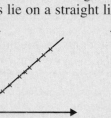

Positive correlation   Negative correlation

- When there is a relationship between two sets of data a **line of best fit** can be drawn on the scatter graph.
  The correlation is stronger as points get closer to a straight line.
  Perfect correlation is when all the points lie on a straight line.

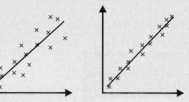
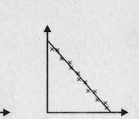

- The line of best fit can be used to **estimate** the value from one set of the data when the corresponding value of the other set is known.

Exercise 37

1   Twenty children were asked to estimate the length of a leaf.
Their estimates, in centimetres, are:

Boys				
4.5	5.0	4.0	3.5	4.0
4.5	5.0	4.5	3.5	4.5

Girls				
4.5	5.0	3.5	4.0	5.5
3.5	4.5	3.5	3.0	2.5

(a)   Construct a back to back stem and leaf diagram to represent this information.
(b)   Compare and comment on the estimates of these boys and girls.

2 The bar chart shows information about the injuries of drivers involved in road accidents at a busy junction.

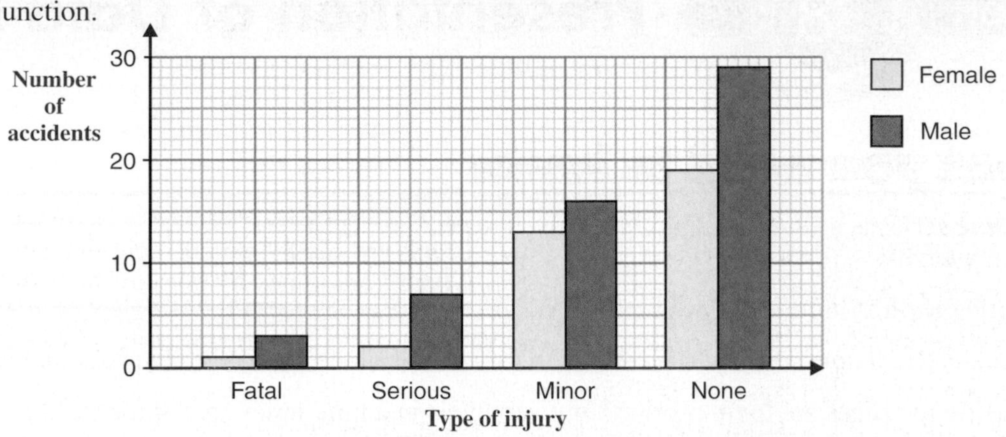

(a) What percentage of drivers had no injuries?
(b) Find, in its simple form, the ratio of female to male drivers involved in these accidents?
(c) Draw a pie chart to illustrate the proportion of drivers with each type of injury.

3

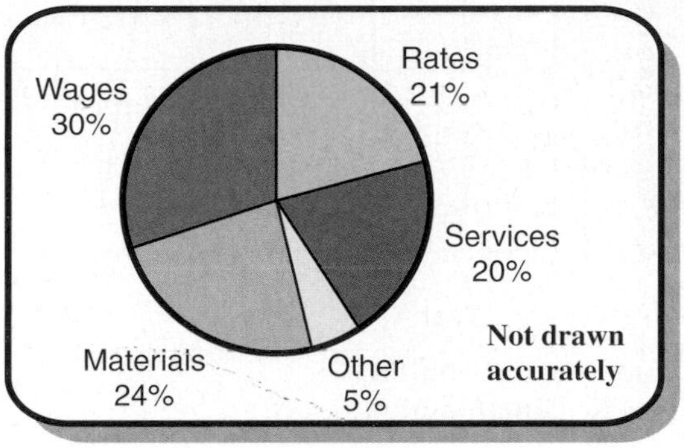

The pie chart gives information about the bills paid by a Water Company.
(a) Work out the size of the angle representing Wages.

The Water Company spent £18 000 on Materials.
(b) Work out the amount it spent on Rates.

Edexcel

4 The scatter graphs show the results of a survey given to people on holiday at a seaside resort.
(a) Which scatter graph shows the temperature (°C) plotted against:
　(i) the number of people in the sea,
　(ii) the number of people with coats on,
　(iii) the amount of money people spend?
(b) Which scatter graph shows a positive correlation?

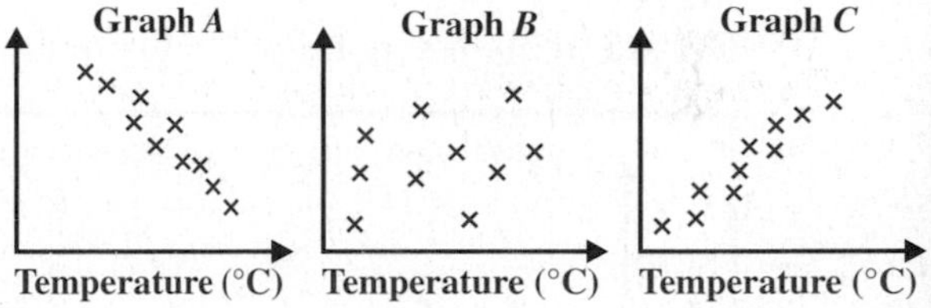

5 On seven days, Helen recorded the time, in minutes, it took a 2 cm ice cube to melt.
She also recorded the temperature, in °C, on that day.
All of her results are shown in the table below.

Temperature (°C)	9	11.5	15	17	20	21	26
Time (minutes)	63	55	48	40	30	25	12.5

(a) Draw a scatter graph for the data.
(b) Describe the relationship between the temperature and the time it takes a 2 cm ice cube to melt.
(c) Draw a line of best fit on your scatter graph.
(d) Use your line of best fit to estimate the time it took for a 2 cm ice cube to melt when the temperature was 13°C.
(e) Use your line of best fit to estimate the temperature when a 2 cm ice cube took 19 minutes to melt.
(f) Explain why the line of best fit could not be used to estimate the time it took a 2 cm ice cube to melt when the temperature was 35°C.

Edexcel

Presentation of Data 1

Presentation of Data 2

What you need to know

- A **time series** is a set of readings taken at time intervals.

> Only the plotted points represent actual values.
> Points are joined by lines to show the **trend**.

- A **line graph** is used to show a time series.

- Variations in a time series which recur with the seasons of the year are called **seasonal variations**.

- **Moving averages** are used to smooth out variations in a time series so that the trend can be seen.

> **Eg 1** The graph shows the amount of gas used by a householder each quarter over a period of 3 years.
>
> The blue crosses show the 4-quarterly moving average values.
>
> A line of best fit, drawn for the moving averages, shows the general **trend**.
>
> The trend shows a slight increase in the amount of gas used.

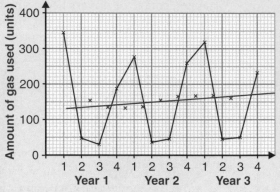

- **Frequency polygon**. Used to illustrate grouped frequency distributions.
  Often used to compare two or more distributions on the same diagram.

> **Eg 2** The frequency distribution of the heights of some boys is shown.
>
> Draw a frequency polygon to illustrate the data.

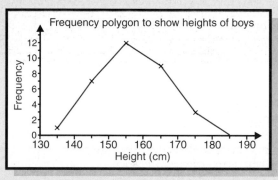

Height (h cm)	Frequency
$130 \leqslant h < 140$	1
$140 \leqslant h < 150$	7
$150 \leqslant h < 160$	12
$160 \leqslant h < 170$	9
$170 \leqslant h < 180$	3

> Frequencies are plotted at the midpoints of the class intervals and joined with straight lines.
> The horizontal axis is a continuous scale.

- **Histograms**. Used to illustrate grouped frequency distributions.
  The horizontal axis is a continuous scale.
  Bars are drawn between the lower and upper class boundaries for each class interval.
  When the classes have gaps between them the upper class boundary is halfway between the end of one class and the beginning of the next.

- Histograms can have equal or unequal class width intervals.
  With **equal** class width intervals: **frequency** is proportional to the **heights** of the bars.
  With **unequal** class width intervals: **frequency** is proportional to the **areas** of the bars.

> frequency = frequency density × class width interval

Eg 3 The times taken by 40 pupils to solve a puzzle are:

Time (t seconds)	$10 \leqslant t < 20$	$20 \leqslant t < 25$	$25 \leqslant t < 30$	$30 \leqslant t < 45$
Frequency	6	12	10	12

Draw a histogram to represent the data.

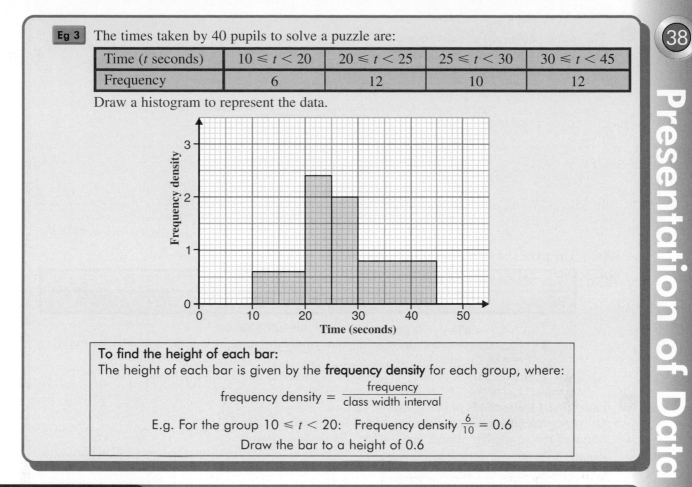

To find the height of each bar:
The height of each bar is given by the **frequency density** for each group, where:

$$\text{frequency density} = \frac{\text{frequency}}{\text{class width interval}}$$

E.g. For the group $10 \leqslant t < 20$: Frequency density $\frac{6}{10} = 0.6$

Draw the bar to a height of 0.6

Exercise 38

1 The table shows the number of units of electricity used each quarter by a householder over a period of 3 years.

Year	1999				2000				2001			
Quarter	1	2	3	4	1	2	3	4	1	2	3	4
Units used	680	810	470	740	640	850	420	750	970	880	490	760

(a) Plot these values on graph paper.
(b) Calculate a 4-point moving average.
(c) Plot the moving average values on your graph.
(d) Comment on the trend in the units of electricity used.

2 The table shows the frequency distribution of student absences for a year.

Absences (d days)	Frequency
$0 < d < 5$	4
$5 \leqslant d < 10$	6
$10 \leqslant d < 15$	8
$15 \leqslant d < 20$	5
$20 \leqslant d < 25$	4
$25 \leqslant d < 30$	3

(a) Draw a frequency polygon for this frequency distribution.
(b) Write down the class which contains the median.

Edexcel

3 The graph shows the age distribution of people in a nursing home.
(a) Which age group is the modal class?
(b) How many people are in the nursing home?

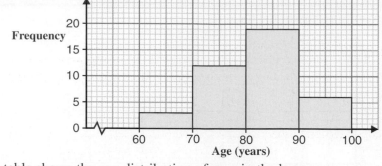

(c) The table shows the age distribution of men in the home.

Age (a years)	$60 \leqslant a < 70$	$70 \leqslant a < 80$	$80 \leqslant a < 90$	$90 \leqslant a < 100$
Frequency	2	7	6	0

(i) Draw a frequency polygon to represent this information.
(ii) On the same diagram draw a frequency polygon to represent the age distribution of women in the home.
(iii) Compare and comment on the ages of men and women in the home.

4 Kim sowed some seeds in her greenhouse.
10 weeks later she measured the heights of the plants.
Some of the results are shown in the table and the histogram.

Height (h) in cm	Number of plants
$0 < h \leqslant 5$	0
$5 < h \leqslant 20$	30
$20 < h \leqslant 30$	120
$30 < h \leqslant 35$	
$35 < h \leqslant 40$	
$40 < h \leqslant 50$	96
Over 50	0

(a) Copy and complete the table and the histogram.

Kim had sown 500 seeds.
(b) Calculate the number of seeds that had not produced plants.

Edexcel

5 The weights of some babies are given in the table.

Weight (W kg)	$0 \leqslant W < 2$	$2 \leqslant W < 2.5$	$2.5 \leqslant W < 3$	$3 \leqslant W < 4$	$4 \leqslant W < 6$	$W \geqslant 6$
Frequency	0	8	9	15	27	0

Draw a histogram to show the distribution of weights of the babies.
Use a scale of 2 cm to 1 kg on the weight axis.

Edexcel

Cumulative Frequency

What you need to know

- The information given in a frequency table can be used to make a **cumulative frequency table**.

- You should be able to **draw cumulative frequency graphs**.

To draw a cumulative frequency graph:
1. Draw and label:
the variable on the horizontal axis,
cumulative frequency on the vertical axis.
2. Plot the cumulative frequency against the
upper class boundary of each class.
3. Join the points with a smooth curve.

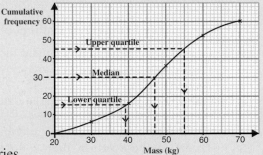

- If the question does not give the upper class boundaries, then the upper class boundary of each class is equal to the lower class boundary of the next class.

- When the classes have gaps between them then the upper class boundary is halfway between the end of one class and the beginning of the next.

- You should be able to **interpret cumulative frequency graphs**.

The **median** is the value of the middle number.
The **lower quartile** is the value located at $\frac{1}{4}$ of the total frequency.
The **upper quartile** is the value located at $\frac{3}{4}$ of the total frequency.
The **interquartile range** measures the spread of the middle 50% of the data.
Interquartile range = Upper Quartile − Lower Quartile

Eg 1 The times spent by students on the Internet one day are shown.

Time (t minutes)	$0 \leqslant t < 20$	$20 \leqslant t < 40$	$40 \leqslant t < 60$	$60 \leqslant t < 80$
Frequency	55	25	15	5

(a) Draw a cumulative frequency graph.
(b) Use your graph to find:
   (i) the median, (ii) the interquartile range.

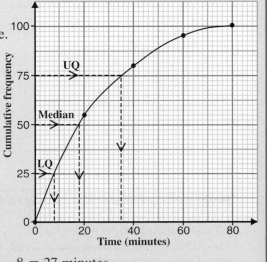

(a) | Make a cumulative frequency table that can be used to draw the graph. |

Time (mins) less than	0	20	40	60	80
Cumulative frequency	0	55	80	95	100

(b) Reading from the graph:
   (i) Median = 18 minutes
   (ii) Lower quartile (LQ) = 8 minutes
      Upper quartile (UQ) = 35 minutes
      Interquartile range = UQ − LQ = 35 − 8 = 27 minutes

- A **box plot** is used to represent the range, the median and the quartiles of a distribution.

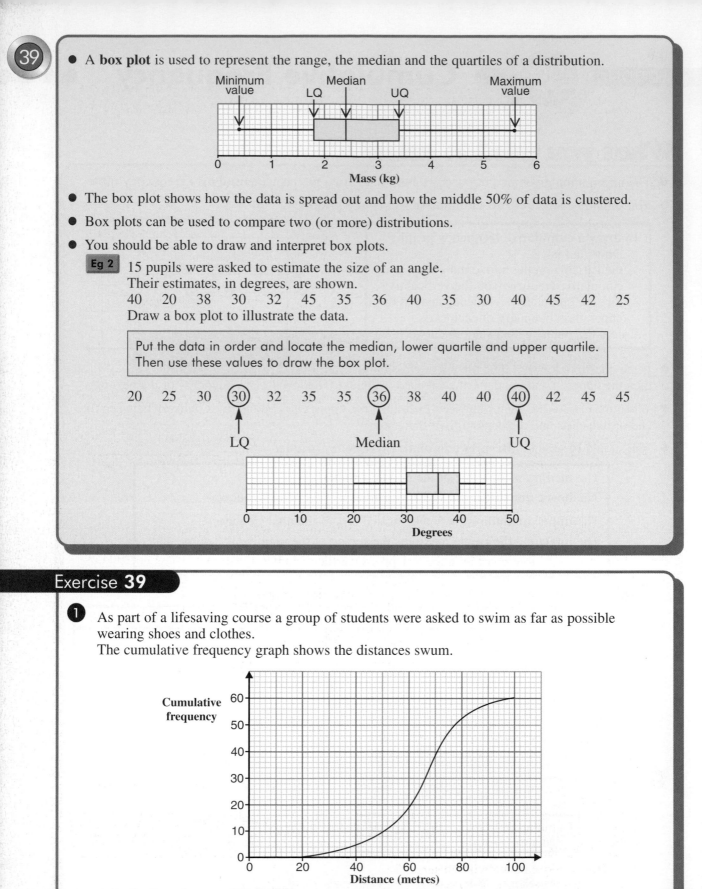

- The box plot shows how the data is spread out and how the middle 50% of data is clustered.

- Box plots can be used to compare two (or more) distributions.

- You should be able to draw and interpret box plots.

Eg 2 15 pupils were asked to estimate the size of an angle.
Their estimates, in degrees, are shown.

40   20   38   30   32   45   35   36   40   35   30   40   45   42   25

Draw a box plot to illustrate the data.

> Put the data in order and locate the median, lower quartile and upper quartile.
> Then use these values to draw the box plot.

20   25   30   (30)   32   35   35   (36)   38   40   40   (40)   42   45   45

LQ   Median   UQ

Exercise 39

1 As part of a lifesaving course a group of students were asked to swim as far as possible wearing shoes and clothes.
The cumulative frequency graph shows the distances swum.

(a) Use the graph to find:
  (i) the median distance,   (ii) the interquartile range.
(b) Draw a box plot to illustrate the distances swum.

② A group of children were asked to estimate the weight of a bucket of water.
Their estimates, in kilograms, are shown.

| 10 | 9 | 17.5 | 8 | 7.5 | 5 | 10 | 15 | 12.5 | 20 | 8 | 10 | 14 | 18 | 11 |

(a) Find (i) the median estimate,
         (ii) the interquartile range of these estimates.

(b) Draw a box plot to represent these estimates.

③ The cumulative frequency graphs show information about the prices paid for computers and televisions.

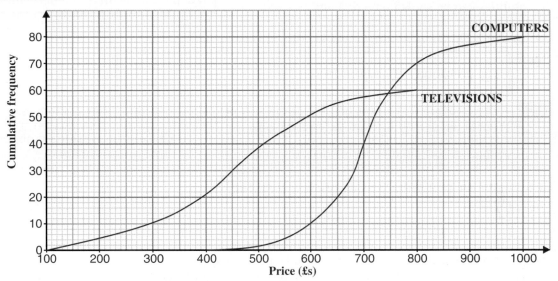

(a) Find the median price paid for a television.
(b) Find the interquartile range of the prices paid for computers.
(c) Compare and comment on the prices paid for computers and televisions.

④ The box plots illustrate the distribution of weights for a sample of eating apples and a sample of cooking apples.

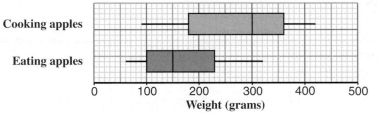

(a) What is the range in the weights of the eating apples?
(b) Which type of apple has the higher median weight?
(c) What is the interquartile range for cooking apples?
(d) Compare and comment on these distributions.

⑤ Fred carries out a survey of the times, in seconds, between one car and the next car on a road.
His results are shown in the table.

Time (s seconds)	$0 \leqslant s < 10$	$10 \leqslant s < 20$	$20 \leqslant s < 30$	$30 \leqslant s < 40$
Frequency	11	31	21	7

(a) How many cars were in the survey?
(b) Draw a cumulative frequency graph to show Fred's results.
(c) Use your graph to estimate the median time.
(d) Use your graph to estimate the percentage of times that were greater than 25 seconds.

Edexcel

What you need to know

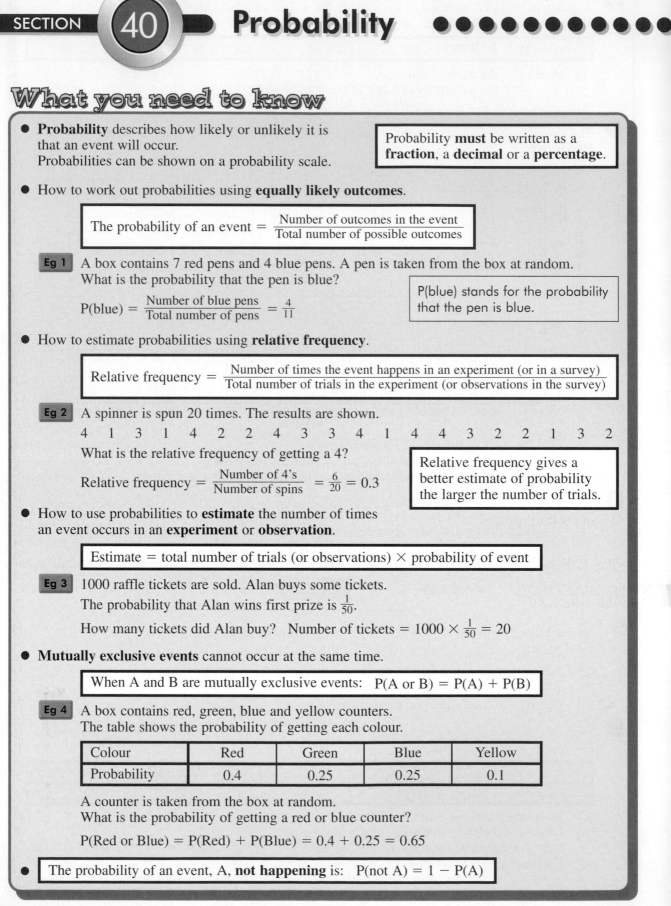

- **Probability** describes how likely or unlikely it is that an event will occur.
Probabilities can be shown on a probability scale.

  > Probability **must** be written as a **fraction**, a **decimal** or a **percentage**.

- How to work out probabilities using **equally likely outcomes**.

  > The probability of an event $= \dfrac{\text{Number of outcomes in the event}}{\text{Total number of possible outcomes}}$

  Eg 1 A box contains 7 red pens and 4 blue pens. A pen is taken from the box at random. What is the probability that the pen is blue?

  > P(blue) stands for the probability that the pen is blue.

  $P(\text{blue}) = \dfrac{\text{Number of blue pens}}{\text{Total number of pens}} = \dfrac{4}{11}$

- How to estimate probabilities using **relative frequency**.

  > Relative frequency $= \dfrac{\text{Number of times the event happens in an experiment (or in a survey)}}{\text{Total number of trials in the experiment (or observations in the survey)}}$

  Eg 2 A spinner is spun 20 times. The results are shown.

  4   1   3   1   4   2   2   4   3   3   4   1   4   4   3   2   2   1   3   2

  What is the relative frequency of getting a 4?

  > Relative frequency gives a better estimate of probability the larger the number of trials.

  Relative frequency $= \dfrac{\text{Number of 4's}}{\text{Number of spins}} = \dfrac{6}{20} = 0.3$

- How to use probabilities to **estimate** the number of times an event occurs in an **experiment** or **observation**.

  > Estimate $=$ total number of trials (or observations) $\times$ probability of event

  Eg 3 1000 raffle tickets are sold. Alan buys some tickets.

  The probability that Alan wins first prize is $\frac{1}{50}$.

  How many tickets did Alan buy?   Number of tickets $= 1000 \times \frac{1}{50} = 20$

- **Mutually exclusive events** cannot occur at the same time.

  > When A and B are mutually exclusive events: $P(A \text{ or } B) = P(A) + P(B)$

  Eg 4 A box contains red, green, blue and yellow counters.
  The table shows the probability of getting each colour.

Colour	Red	Green	Blue	Yellow
Probability	0.4	0.25	0.25	0.1

  A counter is taken from the box at random.
  What is the probability of getting a red or blue counter?

  $P(\text{Red or Blue}) = P(\text{Red}) + P(\text{Blue}) = 0.4 + 0.25 = 0.65$

- > The probability of an event, A, **not happening** is: $P(\text{not } A) = 1 - P(A)$

- How to find all the possible outcomes when two events are combined.
  By **listing** the outcomes systematically.
  By using a **possibility space diagram**.
  By using a **tree diagram**.

- The outcomes of **independent events** do not influence each other.

  > When A and B are independent events: $P(A \text{ and } B) = P(A) \times P(B)$

Eg 5 Box A contains 3 white cubes (W) and 1 blue cube (B).
Box B contains 2 white cubes (W) and 3 blue cubes (B).
A cube is drawn from each box at random.
(a) Draw a tree diagram to show all the possible outcomes.
(b) Calculate the probability of getting two white cubes.

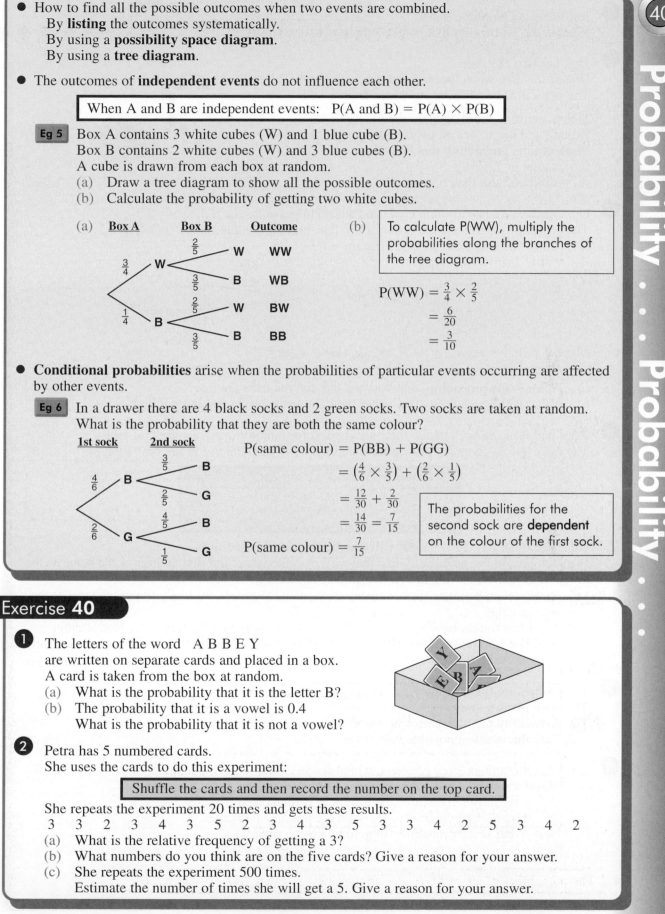

(a)

Box A	Box B	Outcome

$\frac{3}{4}$ W ——— $\frac{2}{5}$ W   WW

——— $\frac{3}{5}$ B   WB

$\frac{1}{4}$ B ——— $\frac{2}{5}$ W   BW

——— $\frac{3}{5}$ B   BB

(b) To calculate P(WW), multiply the probabilities along the branches of the tree diagram.

$P(WW) = \frac{3}{4} \times \frac{2}{5}$

$= \frac{6}{20}$

$= \frac{3}{10}$

- **Conditional probabilities** arise when the probabilities of particular events occurring are affected by other events.

Eg 6 In a drawer there are 4 black socks and 2 green socks. Two socks are taken at random.
What is the probability that they are both the same colour?

1st sock   2nd sock

$\frac{4}{6}$ B ——— $\frac{3}{5}$ B

——— $\frac{2}{5}$ G

$\frac{2}{6}$ G ——— $\frac{4}{5}$ B

——— $\frac{1}{5}$ G

$P(\text{same colour}) = P(BB) + P(GG)$

$= \left(\frac{4}{6} \times \frac{3}{5}\right) + \left(\frac{2}{6} \times \frac{1}{5}\right)$

$= \frac{12}{30} + \frac{2}{30}$

$= \frac{14}{30} = \frac{7}{15}$

The probabilities for the second sock are **dependent** on the colour of the first sock.

$P(\text{same colour}) = \frac{7}{15}$

Exercise 40

1 The letters of the word   A B B E Y
are written on separate cards and placed in a box.
A card is taken from the box at random.
(a) What is the probability that it is the letter B?
(b) The probability that it is a vowel is 0.4
What is the probability that it is not a vowel?

2 Petra has 5 numbered cards.
She uses the cards to do this experiment:

> Shuffle the cards and then record the number on the top card.

She repeats the experiment 20 times and gets these results.
3   3   2   3   4   3   5   2   3   4   3   5   3   3   4   2   5   3   4   2
(a) What is the relative frequency of getting a 3?
(b) What numbers do you think are on the five cards? Give a reason for your answer.
(c) She repeats the experiment 500 times.
Estimate the number of times she will get a 5. Give a reason for your answer.

3 Jeff tosses a coin three times.
What is the probability that he gets one head and two tails?

4 Jack has two fair dice.
One of the dice has 6 faces numbered from 1 to 6.
The other dice has 4 faces numbered from 1 to 4.

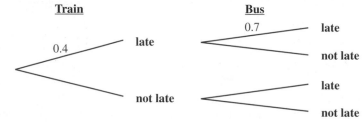

Jack is going to throw the two dice.
He will add the scores on the two dice to get the total.
Work out the probability that he will get
(a) a total of 7,
(b) a total of less than 5.

Edexcel

5 On Tuesday Jim has to catch a bus and a train to get to work.
The probability that the train is late is 0.4. The probability that the bus is late is 0.7.
(a) Copy and complete the tree diagram.

Train　　　　　　　　　　　　　　　**Bus**

0.7 — late

0.4 — late

not late

not late — late

not late

(b) What is the probability that both the bus and the train are late?
(c) What is the probability that either the train or the bus is late but not both?

6 Peter and Asif are both taking their driving test for a motor cycle for the first time.
The table below gives the probabilities that they will pass the test at the first attempt.

	Probability of passing at first attempt
Peter	0.6
Asif	0.7

On a particular day 1000 people will take the test for the first time.
For each person the probability that they will pass the test at the first attempt is the same as the probability that Asif will pass the test at the first attempt.
(a) Work out an estimate for how many of these 1000 people are likely to pass the test at the first attempt.
(b) Calculate the probability that both Peter and Asif will pass the test at the first attempt.
(c) Calculate the probability that Peter will pass the test at the first attempt and Asif will fail the test at the first attempt.

Edexcel

7 The probability that a team will win a game is always 0.8
The team plays n games.
The probability that the team will win every game is less than $\frac{1}{4}$.
Calculate the smallest possible value of n.

Edexcel

8 (a) Bag X contains 3 red counters, 6 blue counters and 3 green counters.
Bag Y contains 4 red counters and 2 blue counters.
A bag is chosen at random and a counter is then taken from the bag.
  (i) Draw a tree diagram to show all the possible outcomes.
  (ii) What is the probability of getting a red counter?

(b) Bag Z contains 5 red counters and 2 green counters.
Two counters are taken from bag Z at random.
What is the probability of getting two counters of the same colour?

Section Review - Handling Data

1 The stem and leaf diagram shows the ages of people taking part in a survey.

| | male | | | female | 1│5 means 15 years old |

```
                          male  │  │      female      1│5 means 15 years old
                                 │0 │9
6   6   6   6   5   5   5   5   5   5│1 │5  5  5  6  6  6
                                 │2 │4  5  8  9
                                 │3 │1  3  5
                                 │4 │9
```

Give three reasons why the results of this survey may be biased.

2 Sylvester did a survey to find the most popular pantomime.
The results of his survey are shown in the pie chart.

(a) 20 people chose Aladdin.
How many people were included in the survey?

(b) Sylvester said, "30% of people chose Cinderella."
Is he correct?
Explain your answer.

3 Grace and Gemma were carrying out a survey on the food people eat in the school canteen.
Grace wrote the question: ***"Which foods do you eat?"***
Gemma said that this question was too vague.
Write down two ways in which this question could be improved.   Edexcel

4 Corrin throws a dice 40 times. Her results are shown.

(a) Which score is the mode?
(b) Calculate the mean score.
(c) What is the median score?

Score	1	2	3	4	5	6
Frequency	7	6	7	6	6	8

5 Mrs Wild drives to school each morning.
The probability that she parks her car at the front of the school is 0.6.
The probability that she parks her car at the side of the school is 0.3.

(a) What is the probability that she will park either at the front **or** at the side of the school tomorrow morning?

(b) In the next 200 school mornings, approximately how many times will Mrs Wild **not** park either at the front or at the side of the school?   Edexcel

6 Jason grows potatoes.
He weighed 100 potatoes and recorded the weights to the nearest gram.
The table shows information about the weights (w) of the 100 potatoes.

Weight (w grams)	Frequency
$0 \leqslant w < 20$	0
$20 \leqslant w < 40$	18
$40 \leqslant w < 60$	28
$60 \leqslant w < 80$	25
$80 \leqslant w < 100$	19
$100 \leqslant w < 120$	10

(a) Draw a frequency polygon to show this information.
(b) Work out an estimate for the mean weight of these potatoes.
(c) Find the class interval that contains the median.   Edexcel

7 To collect data for a survey on the amount of milk bought each week by families, Grant stands outside his local supermarket and asks 10 people as they leave the shop how much milk they have just bought. He repeats this each day for a week.
Write down two reasons why his results may be biased.

8 The table shows information about a group of students.

	Can speak French	Cannot speak French
Male	5	20
Female	12	38

(a) One of these students is chosen at random.
    What is the probability that the student can speak French?
(b) Pru says, "If a female student is chosen at random she is more likely to be able to speak French than if a male student is chosen at random."
    Is she correct? Explain your answer.

9 Ten men took part in a long jump competition.
The table shows the heights of the ten men and the best jumps they made.

Best jump (m)	5.33	6.00	5.00	5.95	4.80	5.72	4.60	5.80	4.40	5.04
Height of men (m)	1.70	1.80	1.65	1.75	1.65	1.74	1.60	1.75	1.60	1.67

(a) Plot the points as a scatter graph.
(b) Describe the relationship between the heights of the men and the best jumps they made.
(c) Draw a line of best fit.
(d) Use your line of best fit to estimate
    (i) the height of a man who could make a best jump of 5.2 m,
    (ii) the best jump of a man of height 1.73 m.
                                                                            Edexcel

10 The graph shows the distribution of the best height jumped by each girl in a high jump competition.

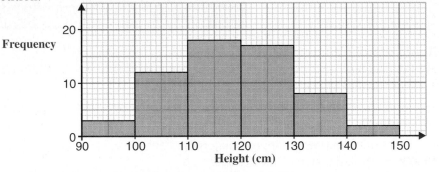

(a) Which class interval contains the median height?
(b) Calculate an estimate of the mean of these heights.

11 A factory makes boxes of cereal.
A box of cereal can be either underweight or the correct weight or overweight.
The probability that a box of cereal selected at random is underweight is 1%.
The probability that a box of cereal selected at random is overweight is 3%.
(a) Work out the probability that a box selected at random will be the correct weight.

All the underweight boxes of cereal are removed.
All boxes that are the correct weight or overweight are put in an empty warehouse.
A box of cereal is then selected at random from the warehouse.
(b) Work out the probability that a box of cereal selected at random from the warehouse will be overweight.
    Give your answer as a fraction in its simplest form.
                                                                            Edexcel

12 Here is a list of the last 8 quarterly gas bills for a householder.

Month	Jan.	Apr.	Jul.	Oct.	Jan.	Apr.	Jul.	Oct.
Amount	£67	£188	£27	£18	£139	£103	£23	£27

Calculate the first two 4-point moving averages for this data.

13 Mr Hulme chose 10 boys and 10 girls at random from his school.
He counted the numbers of different vowels in their first names.
This table shows the results.

Number of different vowels in first name	One	Two	Three	Four	Five
Number of boys	3	4	2	1	0
Number of girls	2	3	4	0	1

There are 1000 pupils in the school. There are 480 boys and 520 girls.
Estimate the number of pupils in the school who have exactly three different vowels in
their first names.

Edexcel

14 The table gives information about the ages, in years, of 100 aeroplanes.

Age (t years)	$0 < t \leq 5$	$5 < t \leq 10$	$10 < t \leq 15$	$15 < t \leq 20$	$20 < t \leq 25$
Frequency	41	26	20	10	3

(a) Work out an estimate of the mean age of the aeroplanes.
(b) Copy and complete the cumulative frequency table.
(c) Draw a cumulative frequency graph for your table.
(d) Use your graph to find an estimate of the upper quartile of the ages. Edexcel

Age (t years)	Cumulative frequency
$0 < t \leq 5$	
$0 < t \leq 10$	

15 Sharon has 12 computer discs.
Five of the discs are red. Seven of the discs are black.
She keeps all the discs in a box.
Sharon removes one disc at random. She records its colour and replaces it in the box.
Sharon removes a second disc at random, and again records its colour.

(a) Copy and complete the tree diagram.

(b) Calculate the probability that the
two discs removed
(i) will both be red,
(ii) will be different colours.

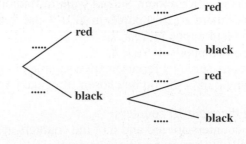

Edexcel

16 Giles has two chickens.
The probability that a chicken will lay an egg on any day is 0.8.
(a) What is the probability that both chickens will lay an egg on Sunday?
(b) What is the probability that only one chicken will lay an egg on Monday?

17 Ruben is doing a survey of the use of mobile phones among students at his school.
(a) Give reasons why a sample of the sixth form only, may be biased.
(b) Ruben decides to take a stratified random sample of 10% of all the students in the school.
(i) Describe how he chooses his sample.
(ii) Give one advantage this method has over a simple random sample.

18 Students in Year 11 were asked to write an essay on "Popstars".
  (a) The table shows the distribution of the times taken by male students to complete the essay.

Time (t minutes)	$10 \leqslant t < 20$	$20 \leqslant t < 30$	$30 \leqslant t < 40$	$40 \leqslant t < 50$
Frequency	8	27	19	6

   (i) Draw a cumulative frequency graph for the data.
   (ii) Use your graph to estimate the median and the interquartile range.
  (b) The box plot illustrates the distribution of the times taken by female students to complete the essay.

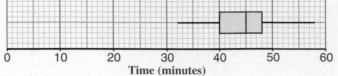

Time (minutes)

   Estimate the median and the interquartile range.
  (c) Compare and comment on the times taken by male students and the times taken by female students to complete the essay.

19 The table shows the distribution of the times, in minutes, that people had to wait for their meals at a restaurant.

Time (t minutes)	$0 \leqslant t < 10$	$10 \leqslant t < 15$	$15 \leqslant t < 25$	$25 \leqslant t < 40$
Frequency	25	21	24	9

  (a) Draw a histogram to represent these waiting times.
  (b) Estimate the median waiting time.
  (c) Estimate how many people had to wait more than 30 minutes for their meal.

20 The diagram shows six counters. Each counter has a number on it.

Anil puts the six counters in a bag.
He chooses two counters at random **without** replacement.
  (a) Calculate the probability that **both** counters will have the number 2 on them.
  (b) Calculate the probability that the **sum** of the numbers on the two counters will be 4.

Edexcel

21 The teachers at Redmount School want to find out what the pupils think about school uniform.
Altogether there are 360 pupils in Year 7 and Year 8.
There are 244 pupils in Year 7.
There are 116 pupils in Year 8.
The teachers survey a representative sample of 40 of the pupils.
How many pupils should be chosen from each Year group?

Edexcel

22 In a bag there are 10 counters.
4 of the counters are red and 6 of the counters are blue.
Ann and Betty are going to play a game.
Ann is going to remove 2 counters at random from the bag. She will not put them back.
If both counters are the same colour, Ann will win the game.
  (a) Calculate the probability that Ann will win the game.

If the counters are different colours, it will be Betty's turn.
Betty will remove **one** counter at random from the 8 counters still in the bag.
If the counter is red, Betty will win the game.
If the counter is blue, the result will be a draw.
  (b) Calculate the probability that the result will be a draw.

Edexcel

23 Alan is doing a survey of the heights of boys and girls in Year 7.
He first takes a random sample of 70 boys from Year 7.
(a) Suggest a suitable method that Alan could use to take a random sample.

The table and the incomplete histogram show information about the boys' heights in this sample of 70 boys.

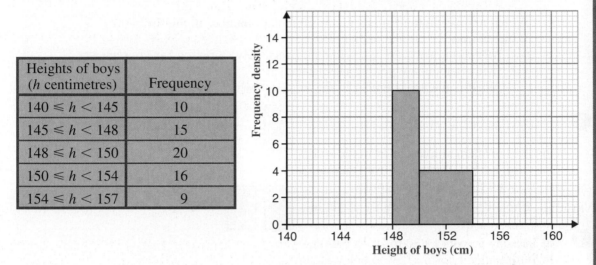

Heights of boys (h centimetres)	Frequency
$140 \leqslant h < 145$	10
$145 \leqslant h < 148$	15
$148 \leqslant h < 150$	20
$150 \leqslant h < 154$	16
$154 \leqslant h < 157$	9

(b) Use the information in the table to copy and complete the histogram.

Alan then takes a random sample of 70 girls from Year 7.
The histogram and the incomplete table show information about the girls' heights in this sample of 70 girls.

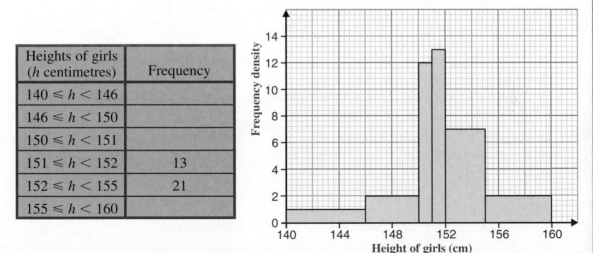

Heights of girls (h centimetres)	Frequency
$140 \leqslant h < 146$	
$146 \leqslant h < 150$	
$150 \leqslant h < 151$	
$151 \leqslant h < 152$	13
$152 \leqslant h < 155$	21
$155 \leqslant h < 160$	

(c) Use the information in the histogram to copy and complete the table.

(d) Use both tables and both histograms to give **two** differences between the distributions of boys' heights and girls' heights.

Edexcel

24 A bag contains 5 lemon, 4 orange and 3 cherry flavoured sweets.
Ivan eats three sweets at random.
Calculate the probability that he has eaten

(a) one lemon and two orange flavoured sweets,

(b) at least one cherry flavoured sweet.

Exam Practice - Non-calculator Paper ●●●

Do not use a calculator for this exercise.

1 Use these numbers to answer the following questions.

3   7   11   15   19   23   27

(a) Which number in the list is a factor of another number in the list?
(b) Which number is a cube number?
(c) (i) Which numbers are not prime numbers? Give a reason for your answer.
    (ii) The numbers are part of a sequence.
         What is the next number in the sequence which is not a prime number?

2 Karina is playing a game with these cards.   **X**   **Y**   **1**   **1**   **3**

One card is taken at random from the letters.
One card is taken at random from the numbers.
(a) List all the possible outcomes.

(b) Explain why the probability of getting   **X** **1**   is not $\frac{1}{4}$.

3 On Tuesday it costs £1.20 to buy a melon.
On Wednesday it costs £1.38 to buy a melon.
What is the percentage increase in the price of a melon?

4 (a) A cuboid measures 2 cm by 2.5 cm by 4 cm.
        Calculate the total surface area of the cuboid.
    (b) Another cuboid has a volume of 50 cm³. The base of the cuboid measures 4 cm by 5 cm.
        Calculate the height of the cuboid.

5 A bag contains counters which are green, blue or white.
When one counter is picked at random,
    the probability that it will be green is $\frac{1}{2}$,   the probability that it will be blue is $\frac{1}{8}$.
(a) What is the probability that a counter picked out at random will be either green or blue?
(b) What is the probability that a counter picked out at random will be either white or green?

Edexcel

6 The diagram shows an isosceles triangle,
with two sides extended.
Angle $RPQ = x°$.
(a) Find, in terms of x, the size of angle RQS.

Angle $PRQ = (x + 30)°$.
(b) Show that angle $QRT = 100°$.

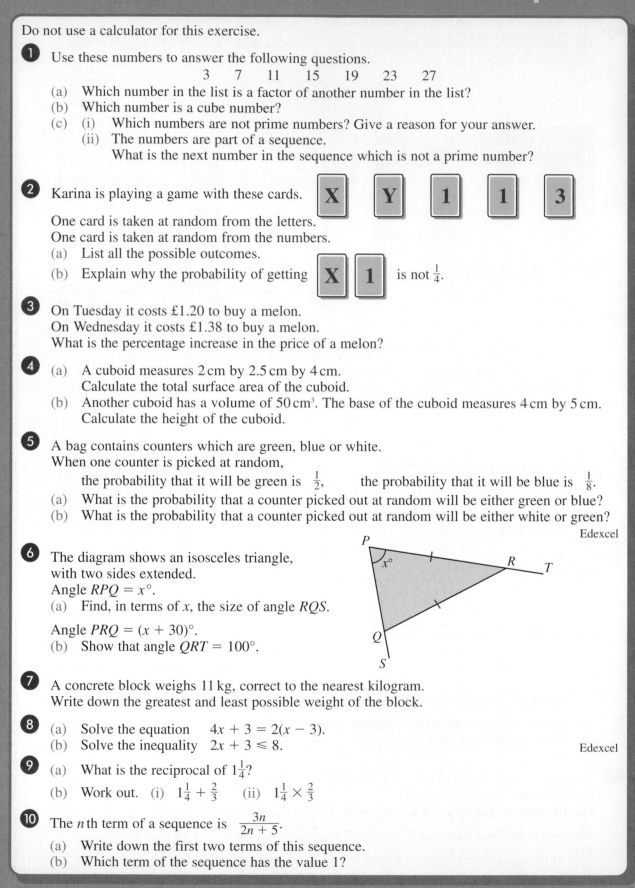

7 A concrete block weighs 11 kg, correct to the nearest kilogram.
Write down the greatest and least possible weight of the block.

8 (a) Solve the equation $4x + 3 = 2(x - 3)$.
    (b) Solve the inequality $2x + 3 \leq 8$.

Edexcel

9 (a) What is the reciprocal of $1\frac{1}{4}$?

    (b) Work out.   (i) $1\frac{1}{4} + \frac{2}{3}$ (ii) $1\frac{1}{4} \times \frac{2}{3}$

10 The n th term of a sequence is $\dfrac{3n}{2n + 5}$.

(a) Write down the first two terms of this sequence.
(b) Which term of the sequence has the value 1?

11 Draw a rectangle 4 cm by 5 cm. Construct, on the outside of the rectangle, the locus of points that are 2 cm from the edges of the rectangle.

12 A sequence begins: -1, 2, 5, 8, 11, ...
Write in terms of n, the n th term of the sequence.

13 Copy shape A onto squared paper.

    (a) A is mapped onto B by a translation with vector $\begin{pmatrix} 0 \\ -4 \end{pmatrix}$.
        Draw the position of B on your diagram.

    (b) A is mapped onto C by a rotation through 180° about (3, 1).
        Draw the position of C on your diagram.

    (c)   Describe the single transformation which maps B onto C.

14 A youth club organises a skiing holiday for 45 children.
The ratio of boys to girls is 5 : 4. 40% of the boys have skied before.
How many boys have skied before?

15 (a)   Write 48 as a product of its prime factors.
    (b)   Write 108 as a product of its prime factors.
    (c)   Hence find the least common multiple of 48 and 108.

16 (a)   Copy and complete the table of values for $y = 2x^2$.

x	-3	-2	-1	0	1	2	3
y	18				2	8	

    (b)   Draw the graph of $y = 2x^2$.
    (c)   Use your graph to find   (i)   the value of y when $x = 2.5$,
                          (ii) the values of x when $y = 12$.

                                                      Edexcel

17 (a)   Estimate the value of $\sqrt{\dfrac{(9.8)^3}{0.39}}$

    (b)   Cocoa is sold in cylindrical tins.
        The height of a tin is 7.9 cm. The radius of a tin is 4.1 cm.
        Use approximations to estimate the volume of a tin.
        Show all your working.

18 The floor area, in m², of 120 houses on an estate is recorded.
The results are shown in the cumulative frequency graph.

    (a)   Estimate the interquartile range of the floor areas of these houses.

The houses on the estate with the greatest floor areas are called luxury houses.
10% of the houses are luxury houses.
    (b)   Estimate the minimum floor area for a luxury house.   Edexcel

19 Solve the equation $\frac{1}{3}(2x - 1) = \frac{1}{5}(3x + 2)$.

20 (a) Solve (i) $7 - \frac{3x}{2} = 11$, (ii) $\frac{4}{y} + 7 = 2$.

(b) (i) Factorise $x^2 + 4x - 12$. (ii) Hence, or otherwise, solve $x^2 + 4x - 12 = 0$.

Edexcel

21 Solve the simultaneous equations $4x + y = 4$ and $2x + 3y = -3$. Edexcel

22 Work out. (a) $2\frac{1}{2} - 1\frac{2}{3}$ (b) $2\frac{1}{2} \div 1\frac{2}{3}$

23

In triangle ABC, angle $ABC = 90°$, $AB = 2\,\text{cm}$ and $AC = 3\,\text{cm}$.

(a) Write down the value of cos BAC.
(b) Calculate the exact length of BC.

24 (a) What is the value of n in each of the following?
(i) $y^6 \div y^n = y^3$ (ii) $y^4 \times y^2 = y^n$
(b) Calculate 3×10^5 times 4×10^{-3}
Give your answer in standard form.

25 It takes 15 minutes to fill a paddling pool at the rate of 12 litres per minute.
How many minutes less would it take to fill the pool at the rate of 20 litres per minute?

26 At a fete Jessie has one go on the hoopla and one go on the darts.
The probability she wins a prize on the hoopla is 0.3.
The probability she wins a prize on the darts is 0.4.

(a) Copy and complete the tree diagram for these two events.

(b) Calculate the probability that she does not win a prize.

(c) Calculate the probability that she wins only one prize.

27 These formulae represent quantities connected with containers, where a, b and c are dimensions.
$$2(ab + bc + cd) \qquad abc \qquad \sqrt{a^2 + b^2} \qquad 4(a + b + c)$$
Which of these formulae represent lengths? Explain how you know.

28 The diameter of an atom is 0.000 000 03 m.
(a) Write 0.000 000 03 in standard form.

Using the most powerful microscope, the smallest objects which can be seen have diameters which are **one hundredth** of the diameter of an atom.
(b) Calculate the diameter, in metres, of the smallest object which can be seen using this microscope. Give your answer in standard form. Edexcel

29 Hugh buys a box of fireworks. After lighting 40% of the fireworks he has 24 fireworks left.
How many fireworks did he buy?

30 You are given the formula $a = bc^2$.
(a) Calculate the value of a when $b = 100$ and $c = -\frac{3}{5}$.
(b) Rearrange the formula to give c in terms of a and b.

31 (a) Expand and simplify $(2x + 1)(x - 3)$.
(b) Simplify $3a^3 \times 2ab^2$.
(c) Factorise completely (i) $2t^2 + 4t$, (ii) $9x^2 - 4$. Edexcel

32 (a) Find the prime factors of 4891 by writing 4891 as $70^2 - 3^2$.

(b) By writing the nth term of the sequence 1, 3, 5, 7, … as $(2n - 1)$, or otherwise, show that the difference between the squares of any two consecutive odd numbers is a multiple of 8.

Edexcel

33 The diagram shows the positions of shapes P, Q and R.

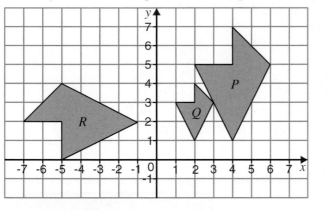

(a) Describe fully the single transformation which takes P onto Q.

(b) Describe fully the single transformation which takes P onto R.

(c) Copy shape Q onto squared paper and draw an enlargement of the shape with scale factor -2, centre $(0, 3)$.

34 (a) The diagram shows the line $4y = x + 5$.
(i) What are the coordinates of the point marked P?
(ii) What is the gradient of the line?

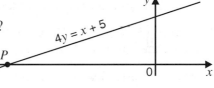

(b)

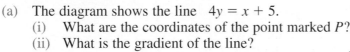

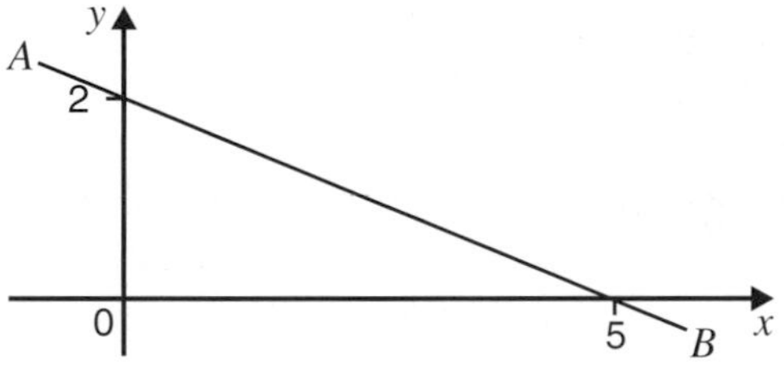

(i) Find the equation of the straight line, AB, shown in the diagram.
(ii) The line CD is perpendicular to AB and goes through $(0, 0)$.
Find the equation of the line CD.

35 These kites are similar.

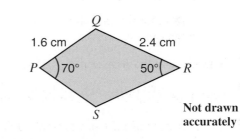

Not drawn accurately

(a) Work out the size of angle PQR.
(b) Calculate the length of BC.
(c) Express the area of $ABCD$ to the area of $PQRS$ as a ratio in the form $1 : n$.

36 A health club has three categories of membership. The number of members in each category is shown in the table.
The club secretary asks a sample of members to complete a questionnaire.

Type of membership	Male	Female
under 18	11	13
18 to 64	30	47
65 and over	7	12

(a) Give a reason why a simple random sample may not be representative of the whole membership.

A stratified random sample of 20 members is chosen.
(b) (i) What is the ratio of males to females in the sample?
Give your answer in the form $1 : n$.
(ii) How many members from the "under 18" category will be in the sample?

37 (a) Simplify $x^4 \div x^{-3}$ (b) Find the value of x for which $4^{\frac{x}{2}} = 32$. Edexcel

38 Show that $(n-3)^2 - 2(n-3) = (n-3)(n-5)$.

39 On a diagram, shade the region which satisfies these inequalities:
$$1 \leqslant y \leqslant 3, \quad 2y \geqslant x \quad \text{and} \quad 2x \geqslant y+1.$$

40 The sketches show the graphs of four equations.
Write down the equation for each graph.

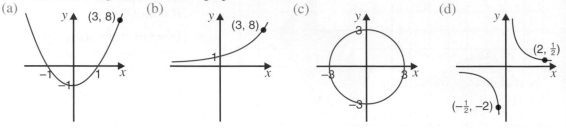

(a)   (b)   (c)   (d)

41 The table shows the number of hours of sunshine and the rainfall, in centimetres, in each of six places one day in December.
The number of hours of sunshine is given correct to 1 decimal place.
The rainfall is given correct to the nearest 0.01 cm.

	Number of hours of sunshine	Rainfall in cm
Anglesey	5.7	0.06
Birmingham	4.4	0.35
Folkestone	3.6	0.42
Guernsey	7.2	0.08
Jersey	6.5	0.17
Torquay	6.9	0.04

(a) Write down
    (i) the lower bound of the number of hours of sunshine in Anglesey,
    (ii) the upper bound of the rainfall in Torquay.
(b) Calculate the lower bound of the **sum** of the number of hours of sunshine in Birmingham and in Folkestone.
(c) Calculate the greatest possible **difference** between the rainfall in Guernsey and the rainfall in Jersey. Edexcel

42 P is inversely proportional to the square root of t.   When $t = 25$, $P = 1$.
Find the value of t when $P = 10$.

43 (a) Simplify fully each of the following.

    (i) $\dfrac{\sqrt{7} \times \sqrt{21}}{\sqrt{3}}$ (ii) $\sqrt{45} + \sqrt{20}$ (iii) $\left(\sqrt{5} - \sqrt{2}\right)^2$

(b) Write $\dfrac{2}{\sqrt{6}}$ in its simplest form with a rational denominator.

44 A, B, C and D are points on the circumference of the circle, centre O.
Angle $ACD = 72°$. ABD is an isosceles triangle with $BA = BD$.
(a) Calculate the size of angle ADB.

AOC is a diameter.
(b) Calculate the size of angle BAC.

Tangents are drawn to the circle at A and B.
These tangents meet at P.
(c) Calculate the size of the angle APB.

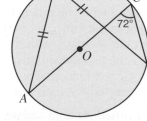

Edexcel

45 (a) Evaluate (i) $16^{\frac{3}{4}}$,   (ii) $27^{-\frac{2}{3}}$.   (b) Show that $\dfrac{2}{\sqrt{3}} - \dfrac{\sqrt{3}}{2} = \dfrac{\sqrt{3}}{6}$.

46 (a) Simplify $(3a^3)^2$.   (b) Solve $\dfrac{2}{x+1} + \dfrac{1}{x-1} = 1$.

     (c) Rearrange the formula $m = \dfrac{3(n+1)}{2-n}$ to make n the subject.

47 **Prove** that when 2 is subtracted from the sum of the squares of three consecutive integers, the answer is always 3 times a square number.

Edexcel

48 $OAXB$ is a parallelogram. $\overrightarrow{OA} = \mathbf{a}$ and $\overrightarrow{OB} = \mathbf{b}$.

M is a point on OA such that $\overrightarrow{OM} = \frac{1}{3}\mathbf{a}$.

N is a point on OB such that $\overrightarrow{ON} = \frac{2}{3}\mathbf{b}$.

Find, in terms of $\mathbf{a}$ and $\mathbf{b}$, $\overrightarrow{AB}$, $\overrightarrow{OX}$ and $\overrightarrow{MN}$.

49 The diagram shows a prism.
The cross-section of the prism is a right-angled triangle.
The lengths of the sides of the triangle are $3x$ cm, $4x$ cm and $5x$ cm.
The total length of the all the edges of the prism is E cm.

     (a) Show that the length, L cm, of the prism is given by the
     formula $L = \frac{1}{3}(E - 24x)$.

The surface area, A cm², of the prism is given by the formula
            $A = 12x^2 + 12Lx$.
$E = 98$ and $A = 448$.

     (b) Substitute these values into the formulae of L and A to show that x satisfies the
     equation $3x^2 - 14x + 16 = 0$.

     (c) Solve the equation $3x^2 - 14x + 16 = 0$.

Edexcel

50 You are given that $m = 1 + \sqrt{2}$ and $n = 1 - \sqrt{2}$.

     (a) $m - n = \sqrt{a}$. Find the value of a.   (b) Find the value of $\dfrac{mn}{m+n}$.

51 (a) Simplify. $\dfrac{4x^2 - 6x}{2x^2 + 3x - 9}$

     (b) Rearrange the formula $p = \dfrac{mn}{m+n}$ to give m in terms of p and n.

     (c) Solve the simultaneous equations $x + 2y = 5$ and $x = \dfrac{2}{y}$.

52 Fred conducted a survey into the times, in seconds, it took for passengers to get tickets from a ticket machine.
The results of the survey are summarised in the table.

Draw a histogram for the information.

Time (seconds)	Time (seconds)
0 to less than 4	80
4 to less than 8	60
8 to less than 16	50
16 to less than 28	40
28 to less than 60	32

Edexcel

53 A sketch of $y = f(x)$ for $0° \leqslant x \leqslant 360°$ is shown.
Draw sketches to show each of these transformations of $y = f(x)$.

     (a) $y = f(x) + 2$
     (b) $y = 2f(x)$
     (c) $y = f(2x)$

54 There are 25 beads in a bag. Some of the beads are red. All the other beads are blue.
Kate picks two beads at random without replacement.
The probability that she will pick 2 red beads is 0.07.
Calculate the probability that the two beads she picks will be of different colours.

Edexcel

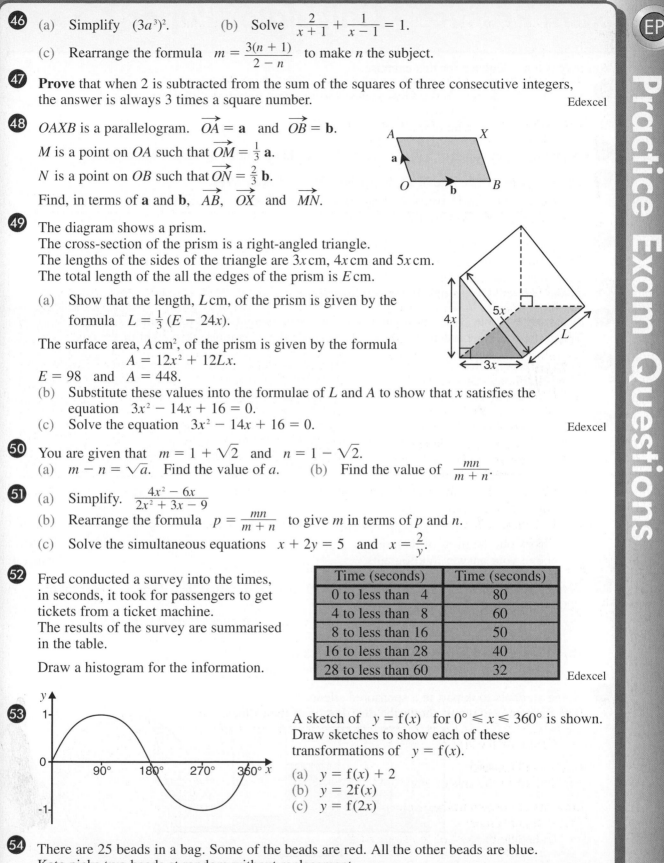

Exam Practice - Calculator Paper ●●●●●●

You may use a calculator for this exercise.

1 (a) (i) Work out $\sqrt{3}$. Give your answer correct to two decimal places.
  (ii) Work out $(0.6)^3$.
  (b) What is the value of m, if $47.6 \div m = 0.\dot{3}$?

2 A pint of water weighs $1\frac{1}{4}$ lb. Calculate the weight of 5 litres of water in kilograms.

3 Cheri is paid a basic rate of £5.40 per hour for a 35-hour week.
Overtime is paid at $1\frac{1}{2}$ times the basic rate. Last week she was paid £221.40.
How many hours did Cheri work last week?

4 The annual rate of inflation is 2.4%.
In the budget the price of petrol is increased from 69.9p per litre to 72.3p per litre.
Megan says the price of petrol has increased by the rate of inflation.
Is she correct? Give a reason for your answer.

5 A rowing boat has 8 oarsmen and a cox. The mean weight of the oarsmen is 73.2 kg.
When the cox is included the mean weight is 71.6 kg. Calculate the weight of the cox.

6 Harvey lives 3 kilometres from school. He walks to school at an average speed of 5 km/h.
The school day starts at 0900.
What is the latest time Harvey can leave home and still get to school on time?

7 The diagram shows a prism. The cross-section of the prism is a trapezium.
The lengths of the parallel sides of the trapezium are 8 cm and 6 cm.
The distance between the parallel sides of the trapezium is 5 cm.
The length of the prism is 20 cm.
(a) Work out the volume of the prism.

The prism is made out of gold.
Gold has a density of 19.3 grams per cm³.
(b) Work out the mass of the prism.
  Give your answer in kilograms.

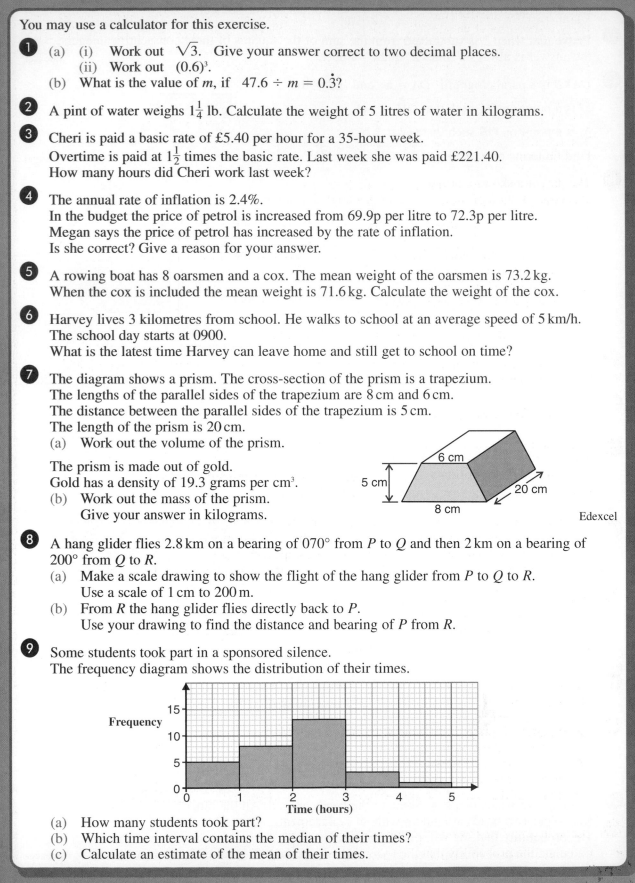

Edexcel

8 A hang glider flies 2.8 km on a bearing of 070° from P to Q and then 2 km on a bearing of 200° from Q to R.
(a) Make a scale drawing to show the flight of the hang glider from P to Q to R.
  Use a scale of 1 cm to 200 m.
(b) From R the hang glider flies directly back to P.
  Use your drawing to find the distance and bearing of P from R.

9 Some students took part in a sponsored silence.
The frequency diagram shows the distribution of their times.

(a) How many students took part?
(b) Which time interval contains the median of their times?
(c) Calculate an estimate of the mean of their times.

10 The table shows the birth rate and the life expectancy for 12 countries.

Birth rate	13	17	21	25	28	30	31	34	38	41	44	47
Life expectancy (years)	75	73	71	68	65	62	61	65	61	56	51	49

(a) Plot the information as a scatter graph.
(b) Describe the relationship between the birth rate and the life expectancy.
(c) Draw a line of best fit on your scatter graph.

The birth rate in a country is 42.
(d) Use your line of best fit to estimate the life expectancy in that country.

The life expectancy in a different country is 66 years.
(e) Use your line of best fit to estimate the birth rate in that country.

Edexcel

11 The sides of a six-sided spinner are numbered from 1 to 6.
The table shows the results for 100 spins.

Number on spinner	1	2	3	4	5	6
Frequency	27	18	17	15	16	7

(a) What is the relative frequency of getting a 1?
(b) Do you think the spinner is fair?
    Give a reason for your answer.
(c) The spinner is spun 3000 times.
    Estimate the number of times the result is 1 or 6.

12 (a) Draw and label the lines $y = x + 1$ and $x + y = 3$ for values of x from -1 to 3.
(b) The region R is satisfied by all of these inequalities:

$$x > 0 \qquad y > x + 1 \qquad x + y < 3$$

Label the region R on your diagram.

13 The total playing time of a video tape is 3 hours.
The length of the tape is 250 metres.
Calculate the speed of the tape past the playing head in centimetres per second.
Give your answer correct to three significant figures.

14 (a) Gerald invests £4000 at 4.5% per annum compound interest.
    Calculate the interest on his investment at the end of 3 years.
(b) Steff invests her money at 5% per annum compound interest.
    Calculate the percentage increase in the value of her investment after 3 years.

15 Bill gave his three daughters a total of £32.40.
The money was shared in the ratios 4 : 3 : 2.
Jane had the largest share.
Work out how much money Bill gave to Jane.

Edexcel

16 Use a trial and improvement method to find a solution to the equation $x^3 + x = 57$.
Show all your working and give your answer correct to one decimal place.

17 The diagram shows a semi-circle with diameter AB.
C is a point on the circumference.
$AC = 6\,\text{cm}$ and $CB = 8\,\text{cm}$.
Calculate the area of the shaded triangle as a
percentage of the area of the semi-circle.

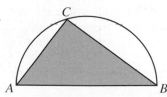

18 Use your calculator to find the value of $\dfrac{29.7 + 17.3}{1.54 \times 68.5}$.

Give your answer to a suitable degree of accuracy **and** give a reason for your choice.

Practice Exam Questions

19 The diagram shows the positions of three schools, P, Q and R.
School P is 8 kilometres due West of School Q.
School R is 3 kilometres due North of School Q.
  (a) Calculate the size of the angle marked $x°$.
     Give your answer correct to one decimal place.

Simon's house is 8 kilometres due East of School Q.
  (b) Calculate the bearing of Simon's house from school R.

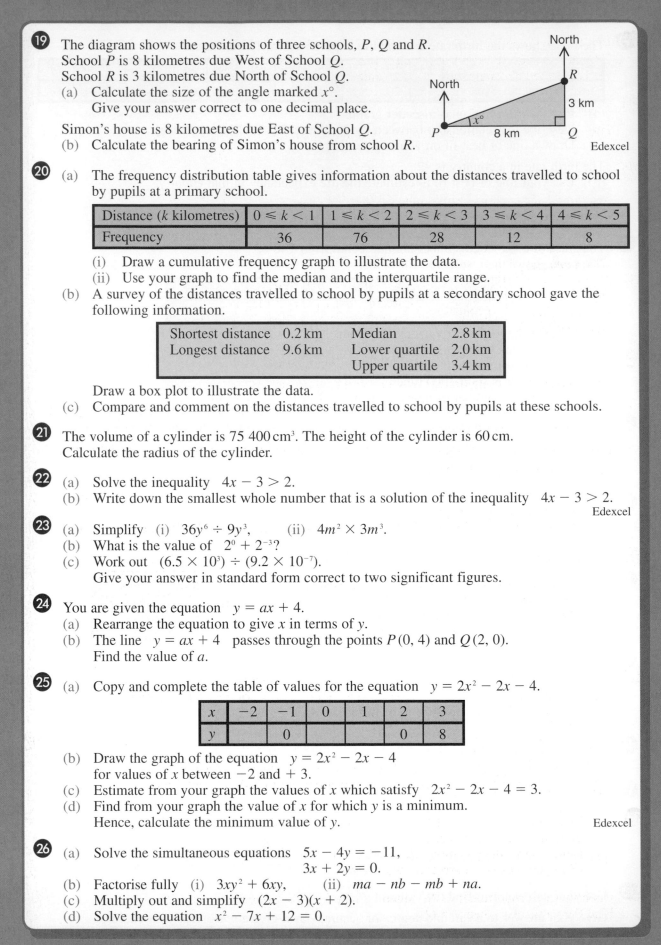

Edexcel

20 (a) The frequency distribution table gives information about the distances travelled to school
       by pupils at a primary school.

Distance (k kilometres)	$0 \leqslant k < 1$	$1 \leqslant k < 2$	$2 \leqslant k < 3$	$3 \leqslant k < 4$	$4 \leqslant k < 5$
Frequency	36	76	28	12	8

   (i) Draw a cumulative frequency graph to illustrate the data.
   (ii) Use your graph to find the median and the interquartile range.
  (b) A survey of the distances travelled to school by pupils at a secondary school gave the
     following information.

Shortest distance	0.2 km	Median	2.8 km
Longest distance	9.6 km	Lower quartile	2.0 km
		Upper quartile	3.4 km

     Draw a box plot to illustrate the data.
  (c) Compare and comment on the distances travelled to school by pupils at these schools.

21 The volume of a cylinder is 75 400 cm³. The height of the cylinder is 60 cm.
Calculate the radius of the cylinder.

22 (a) Solve the inequality $4x - 3 > 2$.
  (b) Write down the smallest whole number that is a solution of the inequality $4x - 3 > 2$.

Edexcel

23 (a) Simplify (i) $36y^6 \div 9y^3$,   (ii) $4m^2 \times 3m^3$.
  (b) What is the value of $2^0 + 2^{-3}$?
  (c) Work out $(6.5 \times 10^3) \div (9.2 \times 10^{-7})$.
     Give your answer in standard form correct to two significant figures.

24 You are given the equation $y = ax + 4$.
  (a) Rearrange the equation to give x in terms of y.
  (b) The line $y = ax + 4$ passes through the points $P(0, 4)$ and $Q(2, 0)$.
     Find the value of a.

25 (a) Copy and complete the table of values for the equation $y = 2x^2 - 2x - 4$.

x	-2	-1	0	1	2	3
y		0			0	8

  (b) Draw the graph of the equation $y = 2x^2 - 2x - 4$
     for values of x between -2 and $+3$.
  (c) Estimate from your graph the values of x which satisfy $2x^2 - 2x - 4 = 3$.
  (d) Find from your graph the value of x for which y is a minimum.
     Hence, calculate the minimum value of y.

Edexcel

26 (a) Solve the simultaneous equations $5x - 4y = -11$,
                              $3x + 2y = 0$.
  (b) Factorise fully (i) $3xy^2 + 6xy$,   (ii) $ma - nb - mb + na$.
  (c) Multiply out and simplify $(2x - 3)(x + 2)$.
  (d) Solve the equation $x^2 - 7x + 12 = 0$.

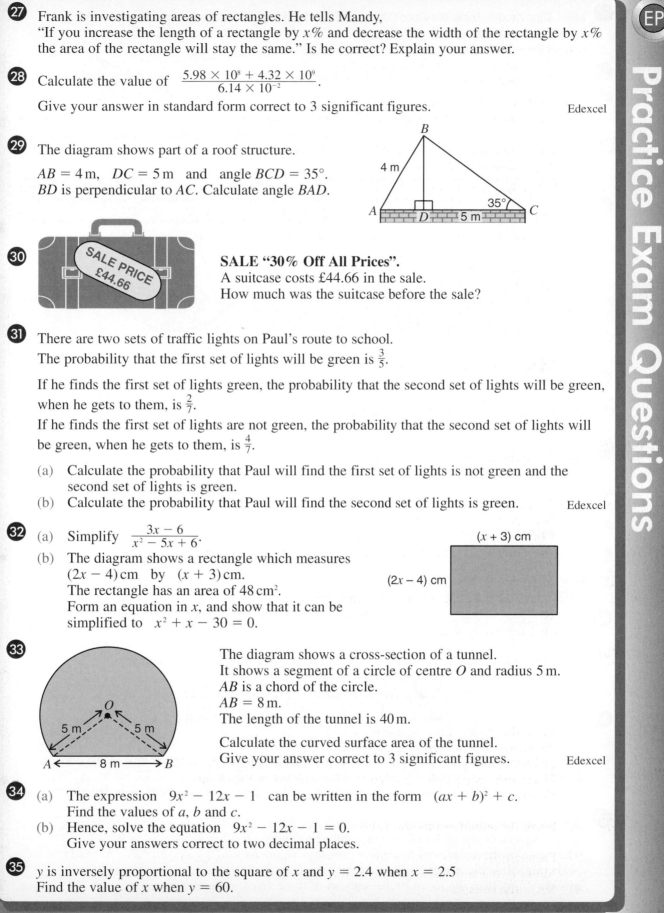

27 Frank is investigating areas of rectangles. He tells Mandy,
"If you increase the length of a rectangle by $x\%$ and decrease the width of the rectangle by $x\%$ the area of the rectangle will stay the same." Is he correct? Explain your answer.

28 Calculate the value of $\dfrac{5.98 \times 10^8 + 4.32 \times 10^9}{6.14 \times 10^{-2}}$.

Give your answer in standard form correct to 3 significant figures.   Edexcel

29 The diagram shows part of a roof structure.

$AB = 4\,\text{m}$, $DC = 5\,\text{m}$ and   angle $BCD = 35°$.
BD is perpendicular to AC. Calculate angle BAD.

30 **SALE "30% Off All Prices".**
A suitcase costs £44.66 in the sale.
How much was the suitcase before the sale?

31 There are two sets of traffic lights on Paul's route to school.
The probability that the first set of lights will be green is $\frac{3}{5}$.

If he finds the first set of lights green, the probability that the second set of lights will be green, when he gets to them, is $\frac{2}{7}$.

If he finds the first set of lights are not green, the probability that the second set of lights will be green, when he gets to them, is $\frac{4}{7}$.

(a) Calculate the probability that Paul will find the first set of lights is not green and the second set of lights is green.
(b) Calculate the probability that Paul will find the second set of lights is green.   Edexcel

32 (a) Simplify $\dfrac{3x - 6}{x^2 - 5x + 6}$.

(b) The diagram shows a rectangle which measures $(2x - 4)\,\text{cm}$ by $(x + 3)\,\text{cm}$.
The rectangle has an area of $48\,\text{cm}^2$.
Form an equation in x, and show that it can be simplified to $x^2 + x - 30 = 0$.

$(x + 3)$ cm

$(2x - 4)$ cm

33 The diagram shows a cross-section of a tunnel.
It shows a segment of a circle of centre O and radius $5\,\text{m}$.
AB is a chord of the circle.
$AB = 8\,\text{m}$.
The length of the tunnel is $40\,\text{m}$.

Calculate the curved surface area of the tunnel.
Give your answer correct to 3 significant figures.   Edexcel

34 (a) The expression $9x^2 - 12x - 1$ can be written in the form $(ax + b)^2 + c$.
Find the values of a, b and c.
(b) Hence, solve the equation $9x^2 - 12x - 1 = 0$.
Give your answers correct to two decimal places.

35 y is inversely proportional to the square of x and $y = 2.4$ when $x = 2.5$
Find the value of x when $y = 60$.

36 (a) Find two values, between 0° and 360°, which satisfy the equation $2\sin x = -1$.

(b) Sketch the graph of $y = 2\cos x + 1$ for $0° \leqslant x \leqslant 360°$.

Hence, solve the equation $2\cos x + 1 = 0$.

37 Solve the equation $3x^2 - x - 5 = 0$. Give your answers correct to two decimal places.

38 (a) Simplify $(p^x)^y$.

Put these numbers in order of size, smallest first. 2^{29} 4^{14} 8^{12} 16^5 32^6

(b) Fred invests an amount of money in an account paying $r\%$ **compound** interest per annum.

The amount of money doubles after n years.

Find a formula for r in terms of n.   Edexcel

39 P, Q, R and S are points on the circumference of a circle, centre O.

POR is a straight line.

The tangent MN meets the circle at S.

Given that $\angle PRS = 36°$, find

(a) $\angle PQS$,   (b) $\angle POS$,

(c) $\angle PSR$,   (d) $\angle PSM$.

Give a reason for each of your answers.

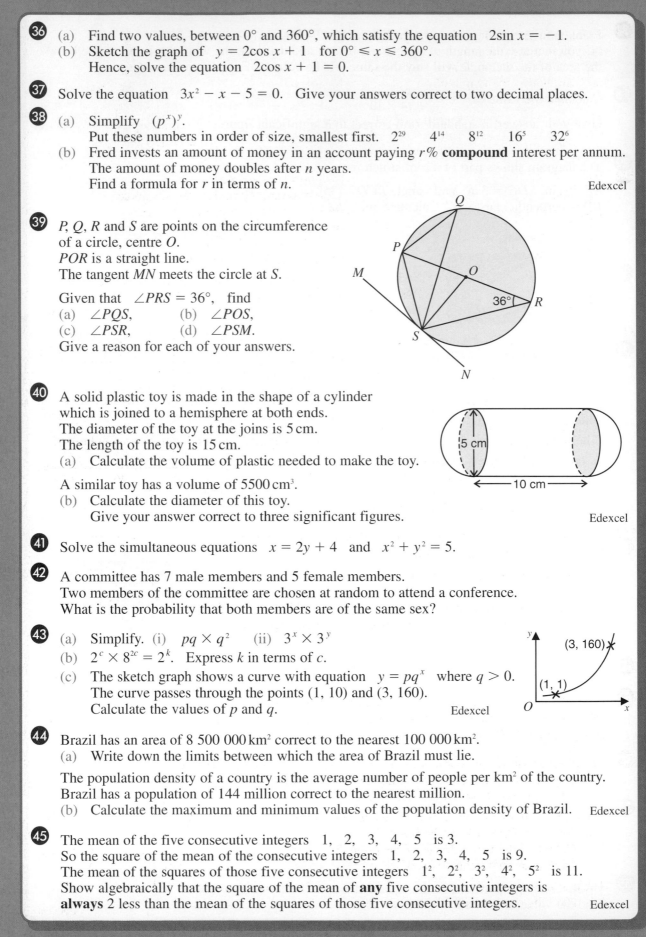

40 A solid plastic toy is made in the shape of a cylinder which is joined to a hemisphere at both ends.

The diameter of the toy at the joins is 5 cm.

The length of the toy is 15 cm.

(a) Calculate the volume of plastic needed to make the toy.

A similar toy has a volume of 5500 cm³.

(b) Calculate the diameter of this toy.

Give your answer correct to three significant figures.   Edexcel

41 Solve the simultaneous equations $x = 2y + 4$ and $x^2 + y^2 = 5$.

42 A committee has 7 male members and 5 female members.

Two members of the committee are chosen at random to attend a conference.

What is the probability that both members are of the same sex?

43 (a) Simplify. (i) $pq \times q^2$ (ii) $3^x \times 3^y$

(b) $2^c \times 8^{2c} = 2^k$. Express k in terms of c.

(c) The sketch graph shows a curve with equation $y = pq^x$ where $q > 0$.

The curve passes through the points (1, 10) and (3, 160).

Calculate the values of p and q.   Edexcel

44 Brazil has an area of 8 500 000 km² correct to the nearest 100 000 km².

(a) Write down the limits between which the area of Brazil must lie.

The population density of a country is the average number of people per km² of the country.

Brazil has a population of 144 million correct to the nearest million.

(b) Calculate the maximum and minimum values of the population density of Brazil.   Edexcel

45 The mean of the five consecutive integers 1, 2, 3, 4, 5 is 3.

So the square of the mean of the consecutive integers 1, 2, 3, 4, 5 is 9.

The mean of the squares of those five consecutive integers 1^2, 2^2, 3^2, 4^2, 5^2 is 11.

Show algebraically that the square of the mean of **any** five consecutive integers is **always** 2 less than the mean of the squares of those five consecutive integers.   Edexcel

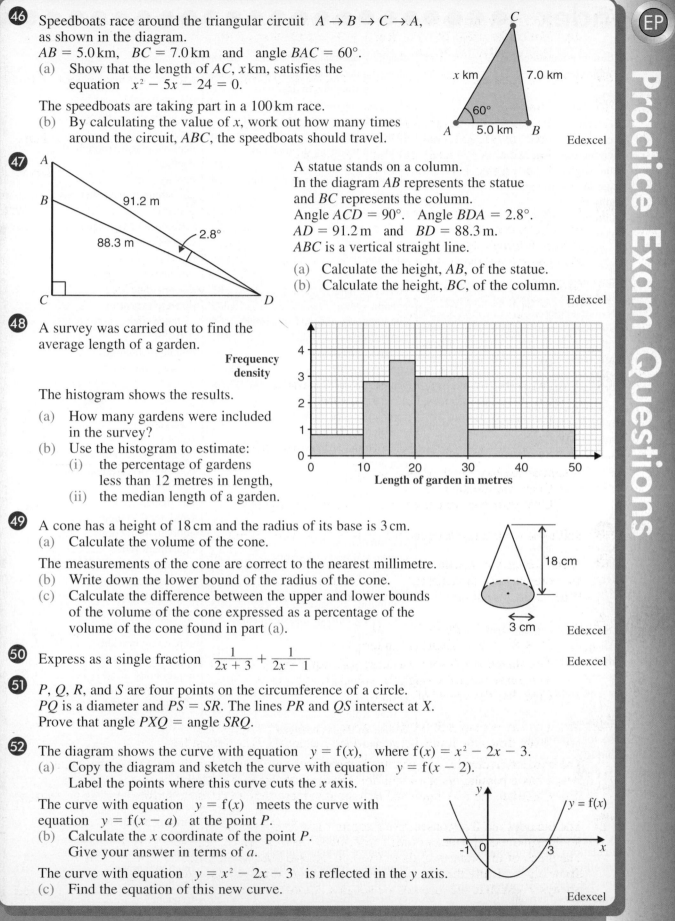

46 Speedboats race around the triangular circuit $A \rightarrow B \rightarrow C \rightarrow A$, as shown in the diagram.
$AB = 5.0\,km$, $BC = 7.0\,km$ and angle $BAC = 60°$.
(a) Show that the length of AC, $x\,km$, satisfies the equation $x^2 - 5x - 24 = 0$.

The speedboats are taking part in a 100 km race.
(b) By calculating the value of x, work out how many times around the circuit, ABC, the speedboats should travel.

Edexcel

47 A statue stands on a column.
In the diagram AB represents the statue and BC represents the column.
Angle $ACD = 90°$. Angle $BDA = 2.8°$.
$AD = 91.2\,m$ and $BD = 88.3\,m$.
ABC is a vertical straight line.

(a) Calculate the height, AB, of the statue.
(b) Calculate the height, BC, of the column.

Edexcel

48 A survey was carried out to find the average length of a garden.

Frequency density

The histogram shows the results.

(a) How many gardens were included in the survey?
(b) Use the histogram to estimate:
   (i) the percentage of gardens less than 12 metres in length,
   (ii) the median length of a garden.

49 A cone has a height of 18 cm and the radius of its base is 3 cm.
(a) Calculate the volume of the cone.

The measurements of the cone are correct to the nearest millimetre.
(b) Write down the lower bound of the radius of the cone.
(c) Calculate the difference between the upper and lower bounds of the volume of the cone expressed as a percentage of the volume of the cone found in part (a).

Edexcel

50 Express as a single fraction $\dfrac{1}{2x + 3} + \dfrac{1}{2x - 1}$

Edexcel

51 P, Q, R, and S are four points on the circumference of a circle.
PQ is a diameter and $PS = SR$. The lines PR and QS intersect at X.
Prove that angle PXQ = angle SRQ.

52 The diagram shows the curve with equation $y = f(x)$, where $f(x) = x^2 - 2x - 3$.
(a) Copy the diagram and sketch the curve with equation $y = f(x - 2)$.
   Label the points where this curve cuts the x axis.

The curve with equation $y = f(x)$ meets the curve with equation $y = f(x - a)$ at the point P.
(b) Calculate the x coordinate of the point P.
   Give your answer in terms of a.

The curve with equation $y = x^2 - 2x - 3$ is reflected in the y axis.
(c) Find the equation of this new curve.

Edexcel

Index ●●●●●●●●●●●●●●●●●●●●●●●●●